Praise for
Roadmap to Resilience:
A Guide for Military, Trauma Victims and their Families

Writing a book that reviews the most relevant research on a topic is easy. Writing a book that is practical is hard. Dr. Meichenbaum has brilliantly done the latter in *Roadmap to Resilience*. Drawing upon 40 years of clinical practice and research, Dr. Meichenbaum has distilled the most salient aspects of resilience and growth into an easy to understand and highly useful format. Focusing on six key "fitness" areas (physical, interpersonal, emotional, thinking (cognitive), behavioral and spiritual) for improving resilience, Dr. Meichenbaum shows individuals, groups, and organizations how to assess, maintain, and strengthen this incredible buffer against trauma and hardship. This book should be in the backpack of every soldier, in the hand of every leader, and on the desk of every clinician.

> —Bret A. Moore, PsyD, ABPP, Assistant Professor of Clinical Psychiatry, University of Texas Health Science Center at San Antonio; Former Army psychologist and veteran of Iraq; Co-Author of *Wheels Down: Adjusting to Life After Deployment* and co-editor of *Treating PTSD in Military Personnel*

This is a really amazing piece of work. I am impressed that this book incorporates so many empirically-based approaches to trauma and resilience. Dr. Meichenbaum is a master of this field, both in terms of knowing the concepts and research, and making them accessible to military service members and their families. Although the sheer wealth of information and possibilities in this book may seem overwhelming, it is set up in a fashion that the trauma survivor can pick out those items to try that they feel ready for, and do their own experiments with developing resilience. This is not a PTSD self-help treatment manual, but anyone who is struggling with the aftermath of trauma can find ways to promote healthier living, and even those with severe PTSD are likely to find many ways to understand and change their reactions to their situation that will help them thrive. Furthermore, I would recommend this book to all clinicians who work with trauma survivors in order to help them see the various approaches they can take in treatment, and consider homework assignments they can suggest to their clients.

> —Richard Tedeschi, Ph.D., Professor of Psychology, University of North Carolina, Charlotte

Roadmap to Resilience is a must read for any trauma victim and for any service member and their family members. Dr. Meichenbaum has hit a "home run" with this Guidebook making it an invaluable reference for building resilience and assisting recovery from combat and any form of trauma-based injuries. *Roadmap to Resilience* is the trauma victims and warriors "go to" Handbook for psychological health and readjustment.

The reader is walked through reasonable, easy to follow Action Plans in understanding the physical, psychological and behavioral complexities of trauma. It is logically organized as the chapters build upon one another with excellent easy to relate to examples. *Roadmap to Resilience* includes numerous Quotable Quotes and "How to" examples that can be developed into a playbook for trauma victims, whether civilian or military. A must read handbook for advice on psychological health and readjustment for clinicians seeking to help victims of trauma.

—Sharon M, Freeman, PhD, MSN and editor of
Living and Surviving in Harm's Way

Many members of the military, trauma victims, and their families have confronted immense challenges in their emotional and physical well-being. Yet, as renowned psychologist, Donald Meichenbaum, emphasizes, the vast majority demonstrate the capacity to overcome these challenges and display resilience. In this very impressive book, the author skillfully summarizes those factors that contribute to leading a more resilient lifestyle, examining fitness in the physical, interpersonal, emotional, thinking, behavioral and spiritual domains. More importantly, he offers realistic practical strategies for nurturing resilience in each of these domains. This book will serve as a wonderful resource to read and re-read by those seeking to enrich their own lives or the lives of loved ones following hardship and trauma. It will also be an invaluable guide for clinicians working with these individuals and families.

—Robert Brooks, Ph.D., Faculty, Harvard Medical School.
Co-author of *The Power of Resilience* and *Raising Resilient Children*

Roadmap to Resilience
A Guide for Military, Trauma Victims and their Families

Donald Meichenbaum, Ph.D.
Distinguished Professor Emeritus,
University of Waterloo, Ontario, Canada
and
Research Director of The Melissa Institute
for Violence Prevention
Miami, Florida
www.melissainstitute.org

INSTITUTE PRESS

Published by

Institute Press
215 Sand Key Estates Drive
Clearwater, FL 33767
www.melissainstitute.org
www.teachsafeschools.org

www.roadmaptoresilience.org

Orders to the trade contact:
Crown House Publishing Company, LLC
6 Trowbridge Drive, Suite 5
Bethel, CT 06801
www.crownhousepublishing.com

ISBN: 978-096988402-6

LCCN: 2012907805

Printed in the United State of America

Dedication

*This book is dedicated to all Service Members
and their family members*

and

*To my six grandchildren
Anna, Owen, Lia, Brayden, Cayden and Ben*

Acknowledgements

I am most grateful to the many returning service members, trauma victims and their family members who have shared their stories of survival and resilience with me. This Guidebook is a testimony to their strengths that they encouraged me to share with others.

I am also in debt to the many military personnel and health care providers who provided inspiration and guidance. In particular, Captain Joan Hunter, Director of the Psychological Health of the National Guard and her colleagues, Major Paul Gonzales of the U.S. Army, Craig Apperson, Colleen Heinkel, Lisa Sayegh who provided valuable suggestions.

Karen Chapple, Janine Armstrong and Chelsea Devlin were helpful in the preparation and editing of this Guidebook. The engaging book cover was designed by Judie Szuets. Mark Tracten of Crown House Publishing has been very helpful in the preparation and distribution of this Guidebook. I am most grateful to him for all of his guidance and support. Finally I wish to thank Dr. Suzanne Keeley for her leadership of the Melissa Institute for Violence Prevention, in Miami, Florida. I am privileged and honored to serve as its Research Director. Please visit our Website *www.melissainstitute.org.*

Table of Contents

By Way of Introduction

Welcome to *Roadmap to Resilience: A Guide for Military, Trauma Victims and their Families.* For the last 40 years, as a clinical psychologist, I have worked with many groups of individuals who have experienced traumatic and victimizing experiences. Some have endured natural disasters such as Hurricane Katrina, earthquakes and floods. Others have been victimized by violence due to human intentional design. I have been involved in the aftermath of the 9/11 terrorist attack, Oklahoma city bombing and Columbine school shooting. I have trained clinicians who treat individuals who have been sexually and physically abused and tortured. Most recently, I have been consulting with the National Guard and Veteran's hospitals that treat returning service members and their families. [Note: For the author's complete biographical sketch, please see the end of this book.] This work is summarized on a website of an Institute for Violence Prevention that I oversee as Research Director (Please visit *www.melissainstitute.org*).

This *Guidebook* reflects all of the clinical experience and wisdom, as well as research findings that I have collected over 40 years. I have a "remarkable story" to relate, one of resilience, courage and growth that individuals, families and communities evidence following traumatic events.

Research indicates that all individuals have the ability to improve their level of resilience following the experience of stressful events, whether they are service members or civilians. In fact, some individuals, families and communities evidence post-traumatic growth and become stronger and develop closer meaningful relationships in the aftermath of stressful life events, whether these events are combat-related, victimization due to intentional human design like crimes or terrorist attacks, or due to natural disasters, accidents or illness.

This book will provide a *roadmap* on ways to improve your level of resilience. We will begin with a brief discussion of the concept and definition of resilience and some facts about resilience. Then we will consider the research evidence of examples of the adjustment capacity of returning service members, family members, and civilians to successfully adapt to adversity. The major portion of this book will be to provide specific practical "How To" ways to improve your level of *resilience* and *fitness* in six important areas:

1. Physical Fitness
2. Interpersonal Fitness
3. Emotional Fitness
4. Thinking (or Cognitive) Fitness
5. Behavioral Fitness
6. Spiritual Fitness

In each area of Fitness you will learn "tricks of the trade" of what *resilient* individuals *Do* and *Do Not Do*. Specific practical steps to enhance your well-being are enumerated based on research findings. These are supplemented by *Quotable Quotes* offered by returning service members and civilians. Distributed throughout are specific self-assessment tools, self-examining *Hinge Questions* that allow you to swing open the gate of possibilities toward personal growth and well-being. These questions are accompanied by *practical* steps you can take and things you can implement *right now*. In addition, there are sections on *Useful Information* that discuss briefly why engaging in such bolstering behaviors can enhance your resilience and also contain additional resources such as websites, agencies and hotline telephone numbers.

You will be given an opportunity to create your own "tool kit" of *resilient-bolstering behaviors* that can help in the transition from military to civilian life. The military has taught service members how to prepare for combat and military activities. This guidebook is designed as a *roadmap* to help individuals to meet the challenges of post-deployment. Although many of the examples offered were created with the returning Service members in mind, these same resilience-bolstering activities apply equally well to the general civilian population.

These same fitness activities can be used by family members and also by civilians in the aftermath of traumatic and stressful experiences. *Appendix A* provides a list of 101 ways to bolster your resilience. How many of these resilience skills and activities do you presently engage in? Which Fitness activities do you wish to refine or develop further?

For example, are you having difficulty in sleeping, relating to family members, experiencing positive emotions and regulating intense negative feelings, finding meaning, maintaining hope, forgiving yourself and others, and going for help? This guidebook provides ways to address each of these challenges and others. There are many different pathways to resilience and what works best for one individual may not work for someone else. You will have an opportunity to develop an individual plan for coping and look for opportunities to practice your new found resilience-bolstering behaviors.

How To Use This Book

There are four ways you can use this guidebook to enhance your level of resilience.

1. You can read the book cover to cover and discover specific *Action Plans* that you, your family and friends can take to enhance resilience in six major areas: physical; interpersonal; emotional; behavioral; thinking (cognitive); and spiritual .

2. You can go to a specific area of resilience that interests you and read about what actions resilient individuals have taken to "bounce back" after a traumatic experience. Learn how others have coped with the aftermath of trauma and loss.

3. You can go directly to Appendix A (pages 191–196), which is a user-friendly guide to all of the ways to enhance resilience. Next to each *Action Plan* is the page number on which you will find specific suggestions of resilience-bolstering behaviors.

4. And finally, you can go directly to Appendix B (pages 199–202) which is a summary of "How to" steps that are listed in *alphabetical* order. Here you can look up a specific need or area of interest and locate the page on which you can find the important "how to" information. If you are in a hurry and want specific information for a specific problem, then use Appendix B.

Both Appendices A and B are like *mini-computers*, providing specific resilience-bolstering activities *on demand*.

I have decided to list each *Action Plan* in the first person ("I" statements) in order to help you see yourself, your family and friends taking specific steps to bolster your resilience. This guidebook is designed to expand your coping tool kit and provide practical suggestions that can be tried by you at your own speed. You will encounter "success stories" of individuals, families and communities who have managed to survive and transform themselves and their surroundings having suffered a traumatic episode.

And one last thing . . . at the end of each of the major sections you will find a request form asking you to contribute other examples of ways to improve your *fitness* in each area. I would like you to please email me at *examples@roadmaptoresilience.org* your suggestions on ways that you, your family members and friends have used to bolster resilience and achieve post-traumatic growth that may not have been discussed. I will share your suggestions with others, but I will keep all suggestions completely *anonymous*. With your help, we will go *viral* and share these examples of resilience-bolstering activities on our website, *www.roadmaptoresilience.org*. Together, we can build "nurturing environments" that will be useful to everyone.

What Is Resilience?

Resilience is defined as the capacity to adapt successfully in the presence of risk and adversity.

Resilience is a broad multidimensional concept that reflects the ability to:

- adapt and overcome

- successfully adjust to difficult or challenging life experiences

- confront and handle stressful life events

- grow and thrive in the face of challenges and adversities

- bounce back and beat the odds

- negotiate adversity

- be stress hardy and mentally fit

- stretch (like elastic) or flex (like a suspension bridge) in response to pressure and strains of life

- recover from or adjust to misfortune or change

- endure traumatic events

- maintain a healthy outcome

Resilience derives from the Latin words *salire* (to leap or jump) and *resilire* (to spring back).

Perhaps, the concept of resilience was best captured by Helen Keller who was born blind and deaf when she observed,

> *"Although the world is full of suffering, it is also full of overcoming it."*

As one returning Vet commented:

> *"Resilience is moving from taking orders or completing other people's missions to creating your own missions and bringing on-line your own decision-making abilities. I have a deeper meaning of life as a result of my deployments."*

And, as often observed:

> *"Man has never made a material more resilient than the human spirit."*

Some Facts About Resilience and Post-Traumatic Growth

"In moderation, whatever does not kill us has the potential of making us stronger."

About 20% of people in North America are likely to experience a traumatic event in a given year. Over the course of a lifetime, some 60% of people will experience such traumatic events that may include experiencing natural disasters, interpersonal victimizing events, accidents, illness and losses.

Following a natural catastrophe or a traumatic event no one walks away unscathed by such events, but neither do most survivors succumb in the aftermath to despair. Most show remarkable levels of resilience. Following exposure to traumatic events, 70% of individuals evidence resilience. The ceiling for harmful effects is about 30% of those exposed.

Research indicates that individuals who had a history of *moderate* amounts of adversities have *lower* levels of distress, *less* functional impairment, *higher* life satisfaction and well-being than did people with no history of adversity. Exposure to stressful life events can have a "steeling or inoculating effect" and help individuals prepare to handle future stressful events.

Exposure to stressful events can contribute to psychological "toughness" having a protective effect when the exposure is limited with an opportunity for recovery. Once "toughness" develops, it can permeate across domains and settings. For example, studies of communities in Israel that were exposed to repetitive rocket attacks compared favorably to non-exposed matched control communities in terms of mental health indicators. Despite exposure to chronic rocket attacks, the residents evidenced *resilience*. Their common ideology, solidarity and social resources of communal life provided a means of protection against stress.

Such resilience is common, rather than an extraordinary phenomenon. People are much more resilient under adverse conditions than they might have expected. A person may be resilient in some situations and with some type of stressors, but not with other stressors. Resilience is more accessible and available to some people than for others, but *everyone* can strengthen their resilience.

Resilience may be available and more accessible to a person at one period of time in his/her life than at other times in his/her life. Individuals may go through periods of extreme distress, negative emotions and poor functioning and still emerge resilient.

Resilience (positive emotions) and negative emotions can occur side-by-side. Personal distress and growth can coexist.

As noted by Ann Masten, resilience does *not* come from rare and special or extraordinary qualities or processes. Resilience develops from the everyday magic of ordinary resources. Resilience is *not* a sign of exceptional strength, but a fundamental feature of normal, everyday coping skills.

It may take some time for resilience and positive changes to emerge.

There are many different pathways to resilience. A number of factors contribute to how well people adapt to adversities. Predominant among them are:

1. The perceived availability of social relationships and the ability to access and use social supports.

2. The degree of perceived personal control and the extent to which individuals focus their time and energies on tasks and situations over which they have some impact and influence.

3. The degree to which they can experience positive emotions and self-regulate negative emotions. Individuals who have a ratio of three times as many experiences of positive emotions to one negative emotion on a daily basis (3-to-1 ratio) are more likely to be resilient.

4. The ability to be cognitively flexible, using both direct-action problem-solving and emotionally-palliative acceptance skills, as the situations call for.

5. The ability to engage in activities that are consistent with one's values and life priorities that reflect a stake in the future.

6. The nature and number of concrete resources (financial aid) and emotional and social resources (empathy, guidance) that is available.

Finally, it is not possible to achieve positive growth by denying and avoiding the pain and other negative emotions. Rather facing, working through, experiencing and sharing one's painful memories and emotions are preconditions for growth and mental remedies. Sharing opens one to possibilities, relief and joy.

There are many different roads to travel and many forks along the pathways to resilience. It is important to keep in mind that these pathways are heavily influenced by one's specific culture. A Western approach encourages individuals to perceive trauma as an "enemy" that should be challenged, confronted and conquered with the belief that they can emerge from the struggle stronger. An Eastern approach views life as transitory and some degree of suffering inevitable, and encourages individuals to accept trauma as a "companion". They are encouraged to feel the pathos of nature and the pain that others may feel and incorporate trauma into their lives. Individuals with an Eastern orientation evidence a more stoic, private response to crises. Their effort at resilience-bolstering behaviors takes into consideration group harmony and acceptance strategies. In short, the pathways to resilience take different forms and it is possible to change course at many points. This volume, *Roadmap to Resilience* incorporates *both* Western and Eastern approaches.

Individuals who are *low* in resilience are at risk for experiencing stress, depression, anxiety, interpersonal difficulties and poor health.

A *Resilience Reintegration Program* can promote *Post Traumatic Growth* (PTG) and physical and psychological well-being. PTG refers to positive change resulting from the struggle with major life crises. Emotional distress is most often a necessary condition for the perception of growth. Many months are often needed for positive change to emerge.

Many individuals not only survive following their exposure to traumatic events (natural disasters, victimization due to intentional human design—terrorist attacks, sexual abuse, rape, illnesses, accidents, losses and combat), but they go onto becoming *"Thrivers"* and evidence PTG. They learn about themselves and what they consider to be most important in life (a spiritual, philosophical and existential reawakening), and they have improved relationships and become more altruistic.

Tragedy can be a *springboard* for transformation. In fact, all of the great religions of the world— Christianity, Judaism, Buddhism, Hinduism and Islam espouse the idea that some form of suffering is inevitable, but growth emerges through such suffering. The stress that is experienced in the aftermath of trauma can act as a trigger or as an engine for PTG. Traumatic stress reactions and PTG can co-exist. PTG does *not* imply the absence of emotional distress and difficulties in living. PTG is not necessarily reflected in the reduction of psychological pain. Such struggles can enhance maturing self-acceptance, courage, fulfillment, positive outlook, sense of purpose and meaning, and improved social relationships, closeness and appreciation for family and friends. Different areas of PTG will develop at different rates. Each person's journey and their *road to resilience* and PTG will be unique. Individuals need to assume responsibility for undertaking and maintaining their personal journey.

In order to determine where you are on this journey from "victim" to "survivor" to "thriver," you can assess yourself by taking the *Post Traumatic Growth Inventory* at *cust-cf.apa.org/ptgi/* (see the APA Help Center Post Traumatic Growth Inventory). We urge you to visit this website and take this Inventory. You do not have to report your scores to anyone. This is for your own personal record. After reading this book, you can take the *PTG Inventory* again and determine in what ways you have changed.

The Post Traumatic Growth Inventory (PTGI) contains 21 items measuring the degree to which an individual experiences personal growth following the struggle with adversity in five areas:

1. Relating to others

2. New possibilities

3. Personal strength

4. Spiritual change

5. Appreciation of life.

In order for PTG to emerge, there is a need to make sure that the level of Post Traumatic Stress does not become too intense or too prolonged. This book provides a number of practical suggestions on ways to turn PTG into concrete actions, and thus, enhance overall well-being. Consider some of the comments offered by individuals who have experienced traumatic and victimizing experiences and who have evidenced *resilience* and *Post Traumatic Growth* (PTG).

"I learned it is not possible to realize personal growth by avoiding or denying my pain. Rather by facing, sharing, working through these negative emotions (guilt, shame, and anger) are preconditions for growth."

"Personal distress and Resilience can co-occur."

"Without emotional distress, I would not have experienced growth."

"I now feel more self-reliant."

"I can now handle adversities and provocations better."

"I can make something positive out of negative events."

"I learned that I am more vulnerable than I thought, but much stronger than I imagined."

"Even though my rules in life have changed, I can handle things better."

"I am more independent."

"I am better at accepting things the way they work out."

"This experience has made me more patient."

"I can endure what cannot be changed."

"I have a greater willingness to express and share my emotions."

"I appreciate each day and the value of life. Life is precious."

"I have a greater sense of openness with others."

"I invest more energy in my family."

"I am more empathetic and understanding of other people's suffering."

"When it comes, I have learned to enjoy my loneliness."

"I am more likely to try new things and try to change things."

"My eyes are wider open. I feel this has been an eye opener for me, and something like a Great Truth about life dawned upon me."

"I can look at life through the lenses of growth, rather than through the lenses of distress and dysfunction."

"Remember that slow can be fast."

"I have a stronger religious faith and a better understanding of spiritual matters."

"My community is closer and more cohesive as a result of this tragedy."

"People say, I am different now, but in a good way."

For further examples of resilience in returning service members and their spouses, visit *www.afterdeployment.org* and view 29 accounts of *resilience* stories.

Evidence of Resilience in Returning Service Members and Their Families

Returning Service Members

- Most returning veterans (approximately 70%), are *resilient*. The typical service member today is healthier, fitter, better educated and more resilient than the typical civilian. Indeed, only 25% of the young adults in the U.S. would make the grade were they inclined to volunteer for military service.

- Most returning military personnel do *not* return from deployment with "invisible wounds."

- From World War I *to the present*, veterans as a group have resumed "normal" lives and are well adjusted. They are more likely to get a higher education, achieve more job success as civilians and get arrested less often than their peers who never served.

- Veterans of war and peacekeeping efforts who had been deployed reported *more positive* than negative effects. They indicated that deployment had an overall positive meaning in their lives, contributed to better psychological adjustment and to higher levels of life satisfaction and higher occupational attainment.

- The majority of veterans (70%) judge the impact of their service on their present lives as "very meaningful" and that their service to their country was still highly important in their lives. Veterans have positive feelings of making a significant contribution. They feel part of a greater cause for their country having helped to protect their family and community.

- Veterans report that their combat experience taught them how to cope with adversity, to be self-disciplined and instilled feelings of greater independence, honor and accomplishment. For example, among aviators shot down, imprisoned and tortured for years by the North Vietnamese, 61% said that they had benefited psychologically from their ordeal. They reported that imprisonment had produced favorable changes, increasing their self-confidence and teaching them to value the truly important things in life. The more severe their imprisonment experiences, the more likely the POWs were to report "posttraumatic growth."

- Research findings of Drs. Dennis Charney and Steven Southwick (Southwick & Charney, 2012) further demonstrate the resilience of returning service members. They studied 250 American Prisoners of War during the Vietnam War who were held captive for up to eight years and subjected to torture and solitary confinement. Remarkably years after their release, they had lower-than-expected incidence of depression and PTSD. To determine how these men handled such a dire life-threatening experience, yet in many cases came out stronger than before, Charney and Southwick studied them intensely and came up with the following prescription for a *resilient life*. As you consider this list of attributes, note that research has indicated that the same markers were found in women who had suffered severe trauma, especially sexual and physical abuse, as well as combat exposure.

  - *Establish and nurture a supportive social network.* Emotional strength comes from close meaningful supportive relationships, a sense of belonging, and connectedness with others who have shared values. Resilience is a *"team journey."*

  - *Engage in positive thinking and feelings.* Examples: being optimistic, this is strongly related to resilience.

  - *Develop cognitive flexibility.* The ability to reframe stressful events. Resilient POWs regard their years in captivity as horrendous, but they learned valuable things about themselves that they would not have learned in any other way.

  - *Develop a personal "moral compass" or shatterproof set of beliefs.* Use one's faith or sense of spirituality as a guiding force. Many POWs never lost their faith and prayed every day of their captivity.

  - *Be altruistic.* Helping others and being part of a group who survived together aided their coping abilities with extreme stressors. The belief in a survivor's "mission" can be a lifesaver to traumatized people.

  - *Find a resilient model in a mentor or heroic figure.* Role models can be inspiring and provide valuable coping tips.

  - *Learn to be adaptive in facing fears.* Recognize that fear and other intense emotions like sadness, grief, guilt, shame, anger are "normal" and can act as a guide. It is not that one has such intense feelings, but it is what one does with those emotions that are critical to adjustment.

  - *Develop active coping skills.* Resilient individuals have a broad repertoire of coping skills that they can call upon to meet the demands of the situation. Sometimes they use direct action problem-solving coping skills and sometimes they use emotionally palliative acceptance coping strategies. Resilient Service Members also express confidence in their abilities to adapt to stressful situations and evidence behavioral control.

- *Have a sense of humor and laugh frequently*. Positive emotions fuel resilience.

- *Keep fit*. Exercise is good for physical and psychological well-being and also enhances brain health and plasticity.

- Many returning soldiers report enhanced meaning and comradeship ("Band of Brothers/Sisters") as a result of their service. They *take pride* in their service.

- They have learned many things while serving that they can apply *positively* in their civilian life.

"Overall, military experience is a positive experience for most who serve. Time spent in the military allows many individuals to develop deep bonds with others who serve beside them, fosters feelings of pride and fulfillment in serving one's country, and it may also provide a broader perspective on life." (Selby et al., 2010).

Family Members

- Currently, 71% of officers and 50% of enlisted personnel are married. Forty-two percent of all service members have children, an average of two children per family. About one million children have had a parent deployed. Forty percent of the children are under 5 years of age. About 10% of the Armed Forces are dual-career marriages, being married to another member of the military. A common saying in the military is that *"when one person joins, the whole family serves."* Overall military families are remarkably strong and resilient.

- The level of *resilience* in military families is impressive given the recurrent separations, difficult reunions, threat of injuries or death, and multiple moves every two to three years for active duty military personnel, and long and often unpredictable duty hours.

- Military families were found to be comparable with civilian families in terms of physical and mental health despite having to deal with the unique demands of military life such as moving often, foreign residence and repeated deployments.

- Among the more than 700,000 members of Reserve and National Guard who have been activated since 9/11, they constitute 35% of all military personnel. Their families face specific challenges of living off base among civilians and as a result are less integrated into a military community with less access to military support systems and programs. Many have had to leave or put on hold their civilian careers because of their sudden military status. These challenges may put Reserve families (spouses and children) at greater risk, as they receive less support from peers and teachers than families of active duty members. Specific interventions across the full deployment cycle can help bolster resilience in Reserve families. Military families who function most effectively are active, optimistic, self-reliant and flexible. They can keep things in perspective and embrace change and adaptation as necessary. They find meaning in military life and identify with the work of their uniformed family member. They maintain good relationships with family, friends and neighbors who welcome and support them.

"Military readiness has been characterized like a three legged stool. The first leg is training. The second leg is equipment. The third leg is the family. If any of the three legs snaps, the stool tips over and America is unprepared to defend herself."

- Military training facilitated the veterans' abilities to establish and maintain healthy relationships both in and outside of the military. Traditionally, the divorce rate among returning service members is lower than the divorce rate in the general population.

- Most spouses of returning service members believe that deployment has strengthened their marriages. Only 10% felt that deployment weakened their marriages. The Department of Defense survey reported that 74% of the spouses of service members report personal growth despite also reporting increased loneliness, stress and anxiety. As noted, positive and negative emotions can co-occur.

- Deployment contributed to the development of new family skills and competencies, a sense of independence and self-reliance. The majority of military spouses reported that deployment of their mate provided them with opportunities for personal growth such as becoming more self-confident in handling problems and stressors.

- As of April 2010, some 37,000 wounded service members have returned home which presents particular challenges, not only to the service members, but also to their families and children. A number of intervention programs have been developed to help families and especially young children deal with parental deployment and post-deployment issues. These reintegration programs include the Yellow Ribbon Reintegration Programs; the Coming Together Around Military Families (CTAMF); Families Overcoming Under Stress-Combat Injury (FOCUS-CI); and the Sesame Street Workshop Talk, Listen, Connect DVD and written material accessible on *www.sesameworkshop.org/initiatives/emotion/tlc*. An engaging book for children whose parent has been deployed is entitled "A paper hug" by Skolmaski available at *www.apaperhug.com*. Also see "*Little listeners in an uncertain world.*" *www.zerotothree.org* (See Action #81 for a list of websites and resources to help bolster resilience in military families). Overall, military families are remarkably strong and resilient. Moreover, the majority of children whose parents have been deployed do *not* evidence clinical disorders. They may show mild increases in behavioral and emotional problems. Protective factors that contribute to resilience in military families include: (1) the availability of social supports; (2) parents who have a good "child sense" and are attuned to their children; (3) supportive schools and; (4) access to assistance and counselling to handle the unique challenges that accompany combat injuries, death, relocation and the like. Military families recognize that "it takes a village" to meet the challenges of the various phases of deployment and the aftermath of trauma exposure.

- For active duty military personnel, family-specific resiliency factors include access to comprehensive health care, education, consistent employment for active duty soldiers, legal assistance and social support services such as Yellow Ribbon, Military One Source, Family resilience campaign and activities, Family Resiliency Training, writing projects and child supports.

- Since the start of the conflicts in Iraq and Afghanistan, *over two million children* have been directly affected by the deployment of a parent. Some 234,000 have one or more parents deployed.

- Children in military families are also typically resilient, even after experiencing significant traumas and losses. Military children typically function as well as or even better than civilian children on most indices of health, well being and academic achievement. They have similar or lower rates of childhood mental disorders, lower rates of juvenile delinquency, lower likelihood of alcohol or drinking abuse, better grades and higher IQs than their civilian counterparts. Military children are in general healthy, have good peer relationships, are engaged in school and community activities and are satisfied with life, having high optimism and a positive self-image. They evidence more respect for authority. They are more tolerant, resourceful, adaptable, responsible and welcoming of challenges. They are more likely of befriending and knowing someone who is "different." They show lower levels of impatience, aggression and disobedience and higher levels of competitiveness.

"If the family as a whole adjusts well to deployment, so do their children. Family and children well-being are closely connected."

"Some of the potential strengths that military life creates for children are the ability to get along with everyone, being resilient and flexible, being loyal and self-sacrificing, having the ability to face risks and challenges, being productive, accepting and living with diversity, and having a need to continue to serve or take care of the world."

—Lynn Hall

"Military brats, my lost tribe, spent their entire youth in service to this country and no one even knows we were there."
—Pat Conroy, the author of *The Great Santini*

"Most military children are happy to embrace the term 'military brat' which comes to stand for being brave, adaptable, responsible, independent, proud, trustworthy, and resilient."

In Summary

- Following combat exposure, somewhere between 10% and 30% of returning soldiers may evidence PTSD, (or symptoms of PTSD), depression, anxiety and related readjustment problems. But, the majority (over 70%) *do not*.

- There are *effective, short-term* treatments to help those who have readjustment problems. But only about one-half of those in need seek help. There is a need to help returning service members overcome barriers to asking for assistance when needed (see *www.PTSDCoach.com*).

This guidebook takes a page out of the playbook of resilient service members and spells out in detail what they do to bolster their resilience and deal with post-deployment stress. Resilience can be developed through focused training and by stress-inoculation training procedures. You can learn to recognize your own strengths and engage them to deal with challenging situations. We all have things we can do very well. The idea is to build on them when you are faced with stressful situations. You can learn to leverage your *resilience* into life changes.

Quotable Quotes

"The number one thing you should know about OIF/OEF Veterans is that they are not the same people they were before they were deployed. But do not assume that is a bad thing. The Service Member may come home more confident, with better problem-solving skills. He or she may return with a deeper sense of gratitude for the comforts he used to take for granted or she may have found a greater sense of purpose or direction than she ever had before. Yes, there are maybe many unseen wounds of the soul and spirit, but there are tremendous resources to help heal these wounds, both for the Service Member and the Service Member's Family, and an ever growing number of people who truly care and want to help."
—Alison Lightfield, Former Captain, US Army Nurse Corps,
www.hand2handcontact.org

"Veterans returning from Iraq and Afghanistan often show amazing courage and survival skills, not only in war, but also at home."
—Armstrong, Best and Domenici (Courage After Fire, 2006)

"I understand that it took time to train myself for a mission of being a warrior and I must allow myself time to readjust to feeling and behaving like a civilian again."
—Anonymous Warrior home from two tours in Afghanistan

"The risks of long-term, untoward mental health problems that follow from trauma experiences are surprisingly low."

"There are a myriad of ways that individuals process and recover from trauma and loss. Any initial suffering or lack of strong emotional upheaval does not imply anything is wrong. The large majority of victims of trauma are remarkably resilient."

Evidence of Resilience in Civilian Populations

- Following a major natural disaster or as a result of intentional human-designed violent acts such as a terrorist attack, most individuals will be upset immediately following the trauma and may experience a variety of symptoms; but they will recover within a matter of days to weeks.

- Fifty to sixty percent of the adult population in North America are exposed to traumatic events, but only 5% to 10% go on to develop psychiatric problems such as Post Traumatic Stress Disorders (PTSD) and related problems.

- There are approximately 150 million women in the United States. Epidemiological data indicates that some 68 million of whom will be victimized over the course of their lives. One in four females will experience some form of sexual and physical abuse and/or emotional neglect. Twelve percent will be raped. Domestic violence occurs every 15 seconds. Some 38% of women will be repeatedly victimized. Yet, of those 68 million women, only 10% (about 7 million) will develop clinical problems that require professional assistance. While impacted by such victimization experiences, most women show remarkable resilience.

- Following the terrorist attack in New York City on 9/11, a survey 5 to 8 weeks post-incident found that only 7.5% of adults living in the vicinity of the attack developed Post Traumatic Stress Disorder (PTSD). A follow-up study in February, 2002 found that only 1.7% met the criteria of PTSD. These findings indicate that PTSD can resolve, allowing individuals to live healthy, normal lives.

- Furthermore, 58% of Americans believed that 9/11 resulted in "benefits" such as greater kindness and altruism, religiousness, increased perception that life is precious, and greater political awareness and engagement. In the wake of 9/11, Americans drew closer, not only to friends and loved ones, but also to their fellow citizens. Americans felt a greater sense of community.

- Following the 9/11 terrorist attacks, Americans evidenced a number of positive and pro-social reactions such as greater kindness and altruism, increased blood and charitable donations, more volunteerism, increased

19

interpersonal closeness to friends and loved ones and an increased sense of a community and patriotism. Tragedy and traumatic events can bring out the best in a community.

- In London, England, following the subway bombing in July 7, 2005 less than 1% sought professional help. 71% had been able to turn to friends or relatives for help.

- Though many bereaved people may experience distress and anguish over the loss of a loved one, they recover, sort through, and adapt in their ongoing lives. Up to 75% of people who are confronted with irrevocable loss do *not* show intense distress.

- Holocaust survivors, bereaved individuals, cancer and HIV/AIDS survivors, torture victims, victims of sexual abuse, rape, survivors of terrorist attacks, wars and natural disasters evidence remarkable resilience. For example, after experiencing a major medical problem such as HIV infection people commonly report benefits and gains such as improved social relationships, new and valued life priorities and the development of greater patience and courage.

- The initial normative response to trauma is to experience a range of PTSD symptoms such as intrusive thoughts, flashbacks, avoidance behavior, anxiety and depressive symptoms, emotional numbing, reduced awareness of one's environment, sleep disturbance with the majority of these reactions remitting (significantly improving) and recovering in the following months. For example, following a sexual assault such as rape up to 90% of victims evidence PTSD symptoms 2 weeks post trauma, but this rate dropped to 47% 11 weeks later and by 4 months later this rate dropped to 21%. With professional help and supports from others, over 50% of these distressed individuals will evidence recovery. Half of individuals meeting criteria for PTSD shortly after a motor vehicle accident had remitted by 6 months and two-thirds had remitted by one year post trauma of the automobile accident.

- Such resilience is *not* confined to adults. It is estimated that 25% of American youth experience serious traumatic events by their 16th birthday. These traumatic events include living in high risk crime-saturated poverty areas, witnessing violence at home, or experiencing neglect and abuse. Such risk factors often co-occur and pile-up over time and it is the cumulative number of risk factors that determine the mental and physical consequences. In spite of the widespread exposure to traumatic events, research indicates that 1/2 to 2/3 of such children evidence resilience and do *not* develop clinical problems, nor get into trouble with the law.

- Following disasters and traumatic events, youth may evidence elevated distress and some symptoms in the first few months, but chronic elevations in symptoms rarely exceed 30% of the youth. The distress experienced is usually limited and transient. Individuals who have some pre-existing vulner-ability (e.g., prior psychiatric illness) or actual direct exposure or loss (e.g. loss of a loved one) may warrant additional help.

- Children and youth who use active, problem focused and engagement cop-ing strategies and who have supportive parents, as compared to using avoidant and disengaging (denial, avoidance, wishful thinking) coping ac-tivities evidence more resilience.

- Parents play an important role in children's and adolescent's adjustment following traumatic events. Parents' support and their child's/youth's feel-ings of trust and ability to communicate with their parents buffer the child's reactions to traumatic events. The parent's encouragement and positive re-framing, emotional support and acceptance, enhance their child's feelings of security, safety and resilience.

- The experience of low levels of adversity can teach individuals effective coping skills, help individuals learn how to access and engage social sup-ports, help develop a sense of mastery over past adversity, and foster beliefs in the ability to cope successfully with future stressors and generate what has been called "psychological toughness."

- The findings on resilience following disasters are *not* limited to Westernized countries like the U.S. and England. Following the *natural disaster* of the 2004 Asian tsunami that was responsible for 280,000 deaths and more than one million displacements, researchers found that the prevalence rate for PTSD was only 6.4% among those from devastated Indian coastal villages. Coping mechanisms existed at both the individual and community levels that enhanced resilience in the face of adversity and enabled normal func-tioning in the majority of those affected.

- In Thailand after the 2004 tsunami, the rate of PTSD in displaced people was only 12% two months post-incident. At 9 months post-incident, this rate dropped to 7%. In addition, the rates of depression and anxiety also decreased significantly.

- On May 12, 2008 in Sichuan Province in Western China, a 7.9 earthquake killed approximately 70,000 people. Despite horrific devastation, the New York Times columnist David Brooks observed that the local villagers were generally up-beat and optimistic, displaying few signs of mental disorders. He noted that,

"These people have stripped down, pragmatic mentality. Move on or go crazy. Don't dwell, look to the positive. Fix what needs fixing. Work together."

The survivors quickly set about burying the dead, clearing rubble and re-constructing schools and other communal buildings. Such community-building efforts helped survivors cope and thrive.

Further examples of resilience were demonstrated by patients with chronic medical and neurological illness. They were asked to answer the following *Hinge Questions:*

- "In general, what helps you cope with the demands of your illness?"

- "Do you have a particular coping strategy? If so, what is it?"

- "What types of activities do you engage in?" "How do these activities help you cope with your illness?"

- "What areas in your life are most important to you and to your quality of life?"

- "What types of social supports do you obtain and how do they help you cope with your illness?"

  - The answers of those individuals who learned to adapt to and cope with their chronic illnesses and who were better adjusted and more *resilient* indicated that they.

  - Adopt a positive attitude and take a proactive role in improving their lives; whereas those individuals with low levels of adjustment look to others to sort out their lives for them.

  - Access social supports and are engaged in social and community activities (e.g., sports and clubs) that provide opportunities to share stories and life experiences other than their illness;

  - Adjust their new lives and be open to learning how to live with their chronic illness.

  - Use ways to reduce stress and pressure by learning how to relax (e.g., listen to music) and to be physically active.

  - Be "realistically hopeful."

Quotable Quotes

"I have to set my goals and just look at that and think, well, I've managed to survive a hell of a lot of other things in my life, and this is just another thing I've got to get through."

"Classical music has never been my interest, but now it really makes a difference to my ability to relax. It's just fantastic. This is a different kind of therapy; you don't even realize the therapy's going on."

"Well, I don't lie around. I rest when I need to, but I like to get out there and do things. I think keeping busy and getting out of the house is good for my mental state and contribute to a positive attitude."

"I get a lot out of being with people, and when I'm by myself, I start getting down and it's harder to deal with my illness emotionally."

In summary, no matter what form a traumatic event may take (e.g., natural disasters, terrorist attacks, victimization experiences, losses, accidents, chronic medical illness), most individuals evidence *resilience*.

The remainder of this guidebook will describe the coping skills that individuals employ to "keep going", "bounce back" and "grow" in the face of adversity.

Fitness Areas

Physical Fitness

Lifestyle factors contribute to physical and mental health. Smoking, poor diet, physical inactivity, abuse of alcohol and drugs and sleep disturbance undermine *resilience*.

> *"I have the capacity to make the choices to take care of myself physically, as well as mentally, emotionally, interpersonally and spiritually."*

> *"The body keeps score of the impact of stress, but it has the capacity to restore and compensate itself. But it needs my help."*

> *"I can make my body an ally in my healing process."*

> *"I can enhance my brain health by keeping fit."*

Physical fitness refers to health-related behaviors and physical activities such as exercise that individuals engage in. In the same ways that physical fitness is a key to resilience in boot camp, it is critical during the period of post-deployment and in dealing with the aftermath of any traumatic event. Health habits in areas of nutrition, exercise, sleep, and safety behaviors enhance *resilience*.

See the Website *www.myhealth.va.gov* for additional information. Here are some specific steps you can take to becoming and remaining *physically fit*.

ACTION #1

Listen to and take care of my body. I should get regular medical checkups, see a doctor when necessary, maintain my hygiene and learn to compensate for any physical limitations. A key ally in my strengthening resilience is my *brain*. It is worth highlighting at the outset that the *brain* is *resilient*. The brain has the ability to heal itself, with your help.

Useful Information

The brain evidences what is called "neuroplasticity" or compensatory processes and "neurogenesis" the ability to form new neurons and brain cells and connections. Rewiring occurs in the brain as a result of new experiences. Your brain is a *"mismatch detector"* that discerns the discrepancy between the demands of a situation and your abilities to meet those demands. The brain is flexible and develops a variety of work around compensatory procedures. For example: individuals who experience head injuries compensate or make up for what they have lost, wrestling new possibilities from their newly imposed limits.

A blind person may develop super-sensitive hearing; the deaf person may become super-sensitive to people's shift in facial expressions; a pianist who loses her ability to read music may gain new richness in thinking about music. Individuals who are born congenitally blind or deaf exhibit remarkable compensatory processes. They evidence cross-modal plasticity which is the enhanced use of brain regions typically associated with deprived senses. They are able to *recruit* neighboring cortical areas. The brain is malleable in response to environmental interventions. As Oliver Sacks, the neurologist observes, "The brain is plastic, even in adulthood. It reshapes itself to fit a new reality." As one neurologically impaired patient observed, "The problems never go away, but I become cleverer at solving them." (See *The Mind's Eye* by Oliver Sacks, 2010). In the same way, an individual can learn to compensate, work around and develop new skills, becoming more *resilient*.

ACTION #2

I can engage in health-promoting behaviors like *exercising* regularly. But I should know my exercise limits and listen to my body for warning signs of injury. Beware of "over exercising" or exercising too much. Over exercising (exercising several times a day at training levels that are at or near maximal can contribute to depressed moods, eating disorders such as anorexia and other compulsive problems). The key is *balance*.

Useful Information

Twenty-five percent of the U.S. population report zero leisure time physical activity. This inactivity contributes to both physical and mental disabilities. Exercise or "getting off your butt" has many physical and mental benefits. Exercise can help brain cells develop, help reduce the likelihood of contracting various disorders like heart disease, osteoporosis, diabetes, prostate cancer. It elevates mood, reduces the risk of depression, and is a stress reliever and blocks age-related cognitive decline. Exercise has a mood enhancement effect. Active people are less depressed than inactive people.

Exercise has been found to be equally effective as antidepressant medications in treating individuals with Major Depressive Disorders and exercise was effective in preventing relapse. Exercise also helps people who are prone to be anxious from having panic attacks in threatening situations. Research also indicates that women who have breast cancer and who engage in exercise regain physical strength, develop a new sense of identity, achieve a sense of mastery and distract them from ruminative brooding on their illness. Physical exercise has been found to decrease smoking, alcohol, caffeine and junk food consumption, and even reduced impulsive spending, watching television and the tendency to leave dirty dishes in the sink. (For more examples, search for "Benefits of Exercise" on the Internet). At this point, it is not clear which form of exercise (aerobic exercise or weight training) affords the most health benefits. We do know that exercise can help buffer how the brain is going to respond to future stressors. Exercise can promote growth in the brain ("neurogenesis").

It is recommended that individuals engage in moderate aerobic exercise like brisk walking at least 5 half-hour periods a week or vigorous exercise periods of 20 minutes at least 3 times a week. But even small amounts of exercise can make a difference right away. Doctors now prescribe exercise as a way to treat depression (every 50 minutes of exercise per week has been found to reduce levels of depression up to 50%) and for anxiety and anger problems. Individuals who worry about their anxiety symptoms can spiral into fears which increase their anxiety and so on. Exercise, no matter how minimal to begin with can help break this cycle. SO START MOVING!

As Joan Borysenko observes:

> "Too many people confine their exercise to jumping to conclusions, running up bills, stretching the truth, bending over backward, lying down on the job, side-stepping responsibility, and pushing their luck."

Individuals who avoid exercise and who tend to cope by engaging in persistent avoidance behavior need to move from what has been described as a TRAP to TRAC.

T	-	Trigger
R	-	Response
AP	-	Avoidance Pattern

to

T	-	Trigger
R	-	Response
AC	-	Alternative Coping

For example, instead of withdrawing and becoming depressed, there is a need for *behaviour activation* (BA) in the form of some type of exercise and physical engagement. Keeping an Activity Chart and building in a reinforcement "pay-off" program for such alternative coping helps to develop daily routines that strengthen *resilience*.

ACTION # 3

I need to get good uninterrupted sleep. Sleep disturbance strongly increases negative moods and decreases positive emotions. Similarly, high levels of emotional arousal can disturb sleep. Sleep deprivation can induce neurochemical changes similar to depression and impairs my quality of life.

Useful Information

Sleep disturbance is the most frequent non-wound or non-injury related concern reported by deployed service members during post-deployment. Sleep disturbances, nightmares, fear of sleeping are part of a normal and typical response to trauma. Rates of sleep disruption usually decline within 1-3 months post trauma. If sleep disturbances persist, then the individual should seek professional help as in the case of insomnia, trauma-related nightmares, sleep apnea and narcolepsy. Sleep disturbance often precede the onset of depression and Post Traumatic Stress Disorder (PTSD).

Sleep has a protective effect on the brain. Most people need 7 to 8 hours of sleep each night. It may take 3 to 6 months to readjust one's sleep pattern (for example, shifting from a 4 hour sleep pattern while deployed to a 7 to 8 hour sleep pattern during post-deployment or after experiencing a traumatic event). Sleep disturbance can contribute to mood and behavior problems. The following steps enumerate ways to break this "vicious cycle" between sleep disturbance and mood and behavior difficulties.

How To: Improve Sleep Behavior

1. Determine your individualized *Sleep Efficiency* score by keeping a sleep diary for 7 to 14 days. Record the times you went to sleep and woke up for a week or two. Also jot down any times you were aware of waking up in the middle of the night. Your Sleep Efficiency Score (SE) reflects the Total Sleep Time (TST) and the Total Time in Bed (TIB). *SE=TST/TIB X* 100

2. Maintain a regular sleep schedule. Establish a regular time for going to bed and getting up in the morning. Have a routine wake up time, 7 days a week. A regular wake-up time in the morning will help set your "biological clock" and lead to regular sleep onset. Limit time spent in bed prior to sleep.

3. Have a comfortable sleep environment. Make sure your bed is comfortable and that your room is quiet and set at a comfortable temperature. Turn off all lights (television, computers.) Use eye shades, if necessary.

4. Use your bed only for sleep and sex. Do not use the bed for eating or watching TV.

5. Have a simple relaxing wind down 30 to 60 minutes routine before you go to bed. Outside of the bed, do something relaxing in the half-hour before bedtime. For example, listen to soothing music, read, or do some form of relaxation exercises (meditation, yoga).

6. Do not use alcohol or non-prescription drugs to help you fall asleep. A small amount of alcohol can promote the onset of sleep, but as alcohol is metabolized sleep becomes disturbed and more difficult. Thus, alcohol is a poor sleep aid. Sleep medications are effective only *temporarily*, losing their effectiveness in about 2 to 4 weeks when taken regularly. Over time, sleeping pills can make sleep problems worse. When sleeping pills have been used for a long period, withdrawal from the medication can lead to an insomnia rebound. There are however, some prescription medications such as Prazosin® that have been found to reduce nightmare intensity and frequency, in addition to improving total sleep quality without causing excessive sedation. Such medications should *only* be taken with a doctor's supervision.

7. Things to avoid before bedtime.

   a. Avoid caffeine 4-6 hours before bedtime. Caffeine disturbs sleep. Caffeine is found in coffee, tea, soda, chocolate and many over the counter medications such as Excedrin. Caffeine and also tobacco increase heart rate and respiration rates that interfere with sleep.

   b. Avoid nicotine before bedtime and during the night since it is a stimulant.

   c. Avoid drinking fluids and high energy drinks before bedtime, so that sleep is not disturbed by the need to use the bathroom.

   d. Avoid eating a large meal before bedtime. However, a light soothing snack facilitates sleep. A glass of warm milk or a bowl of cereal can promote sleep.

   e. Avoid taking a hot bath shortly before bedtime since it tends to increase alertness. However, spending 20 minutes in a tub of hot water an hour prior to bedtime can promote sleep by lowering body temperature that aids sleep onset.

   f. Avoid vigorous exercise within 2 hours before bedtime which elevates nervous system activity and interferes with sleep onset. However, maintaining a regular exercise schedule will enhance general well-being and foster sleep.

8. Do not nap during the day. Save the need to fulfill the body's sleep requirements to your night time sleep activity. If you do nap, be sure to schedule naps before 3:00 P.M. Go to sleep at bedtime when sleepy.

9. Do not watch the clock as you try to fall asleep. Watching the clock and obsessing about the time will just make it more difficult to sleep. Position clocks out of sight, as clock watching can create anxiety about lack of sleep.

10. If you are unable to fall asleep (in some 20 minutes) do not remain in bed. Get up and move to another room and stay up and read or try another quiet activity until you are sleepy again. The goal is to associate the bed with falling asleep quickly.

11. Do not have worry time in bed. If worrying or ruminating are interfering with your sleep, designate a "worry chair" that is not too comfortable in another room and use that chair as the location for worrying and ruminating. Plan time earlier in the day to review and deal with any problems. Worrying in bed can interfere with sleep onset and cause you to have shallow sleep. Tell yourself that you will postpone thinking or worrying about anything until the next day. While you are in the "worry chair" you can write down your thoughts and feelings about what is bothering you and you can talk them over with a friend the next day.

12. Do not try too hard to fall asleep. You will frustrate yourself, leading to a paradoxical effect and work yourself into an anxious state of mind. Instead, tell yourself, *It is okay if I get only a few hours of sleep tonight. I can catch up the next few nights.* This change in expectation will free you up to relax. The harder you try to go to sleep, the harder it will be to induce sleep.

13. Do not go to bed mad. Instead, generate a "gratitude" list of things for which you are grateful. Use positive images to recall these events (See Action #30).

14. Use a variety of coping strategies like meditation, mindfulness skills and pleasant imagery to relax. The positive image can be a place you would like to go on a vacation, or something relaxing you have done in the past. See if you can "switch mental channels" and tune into pleasant relaxing scenes (See Action #41).

15. If you cannot fall asleep, just lie in bed and try to rest. Tell yourself that "it is okay to just rest." Give up the struggle to go to sleep. Let a restful state set in which may induce sleep.

16. Avoid "chasing" sleep. If these sleep hygiene and stimulus control procedures do *not* work, then try consolidating and restricting your sleep patterns. Sleep restriction is accomplished by establishing a fixed wake up time and then limit the time in bed as determined from your Sleep Diary. If you need to wake up at 7 A.M. and you average 5 hours of sleep you would have to go to bed at 2 A.M. As this sleep time improves to 90% of the five hours, you can go to bed earlier in increments of 15 minutes. Such sleep management procedures are usually effective.

17. Include your partner as a collaborator in implementing this sleep plan.

18. Establish a bedtime ritual with your partner (if you have one), whenever possible. Go to bed at the same time so that you can share intimacy, "pillow talk" and a satisfying sexual, love-making relationship that contributes to sound sleep.

How To: Deal with Nightmares

It is not unusual for individuals to have nightmares. As many as 25% of individuals have a nightmare at least once a month. Nightmares often follow trauma exposure and victimization experiences. The content of trauma-related nightmares tend to change over time, shifting from memories and reminders that were directly related to the trauma to more generally anxious dreams along the themes of loss of control, guilt, shame, abandonment and the like. Remind yourself that nightmares are "night time spoilers." Remember that all bad dreams are normal and common among those who have experienced stressful events. Nightmares can be disruptive, but they *cannot* hurt you and you can gain control over nightmares.

A procedure that has helped individuals with nightmares is called *imagery retraining.* The individual who experiences repetitive nightmares is asked to *re-script* his/her nightmare. Imagery Retraining has individuals write down their nightmares and then asks them to change them in any way they wish, and then to write out their new dream. By changing the ending, or by inserting protective features, or by transforming features of the dream, or distancing oneself as if watching it on a television, the dreamer is able to develop mastery over the nightmare. Individuals are encouraged to practice the new dream at least twice a day for 10 minutes each time. (See Action #37 for other examples of "writing cures").

ACTION #4

I should eat a balanced healthy diet and where indicated add supplements to my diet. Select my food intake carefully.

1. Choose a "rainbow diet" of multicolored vegetables and fruits.

2. Include in my diet some cold deep-seawater fish like salmon which contains beneficial omega-3 fish oils and avoid fish that have mercury levels (swordfish, mackerel, and shark).

3. Reduce excessive calorie intake that contributes to obesity that is a high risk for multiple physical and cognitive risks. Stay away from junk foods.

4. Curb intake of caffeine. Ingesting 250 mg. of caffeine in a short period of time (a couple of energy drinks) contribute to anxiety, nightmares, sleep-lessness, and irritability.

5. Supplement my food intake with fish oil (omega-3 fatty acids), unless counter-indicated due to medical conditions such as gastrointestinal symp-toms, bleeding disorders or taking other medications such as anticoagulants. It is best to check with your doctor when adding supplements to your diet.

Useful Information

People who eat right think more clearly, have more energy, and are able to fight off disease. Adequate and proper nutrition are necessary to maintain resilience. When you skip meals like breakfast or lunch, your blood sugar level drops, increasing your level of irritability and fatigue and it reduces your ability to think clearly. Junk food can increase the likelihood of mood swings. Eating well-balanced meals boosts your *resilience*.

ACTION #5

I should avoid tobacco, mood-altering recreational drugs and excessive use of alcohol.

Useful Information

It is estimated that 7% of individuals in military settings have *Substance-abuse Disorders* and overall this translates into approximately 1.8 million veterans affected by sub-stance abuse. A survey of 16,000 active-duty military personnel revealed that 43% iden-tified themselves as "binge drinkers," which is defined as the consumption of five or more standard drinks in one sitting for men; four or more drinks for women, at least once in the preceding 30 days. Individuals who engage in binge drinking are five times as likely to have interpersonal problems with their significant others, five times as likely to admit that their spouse had threatened to leave or did actually leave the re-lationship, and nine times as likely to report they were asked to leave by their partner.

Note: one standard drink is equivalent to 12 ounces of beer or cooler (5% alcohol), 5 ounces of wine (12% alcohol) or 1.5 ounces of 80-proof spirits (40% alcohol). The average person metabolizes about 1 standard drink per hour.

What is Your Drinking Pattern?

1. How many times in the past year have you had five or more drinks in a day for men or four more drinks a day for women?

2. On average how many *days* do you have an alcoholic drink?

3. On a typical day, how many drinks do you have?

4. Do you have more than 14 drinks a week (for men), and seven drinks a week (for women)? (Men and women metabolize alcohol differently).

Do You Drink Too Much?

There are a number of self-report scales where you can determine if your drinking alcohol is a problem for you. You can take these assessment tools and keep the scores *confidential*. These are listed here for your own private analysis. Also included are websites where you can find helpful information. Let us begin with the simple and straightforward widely used *CAGE* (see italicized words below in questions) measure.

Answer each of these four questions *yes* or *no*.

1. Have you ever felt you should *cut down* on your drinking?

2. Have people *annoyed* you by criticizing your drinking?

3. Have you ever felt *guilty* about your drinking?

4. Have you ever had a drink first thing in the morning to steady your nerves or get rid of a hangover (*eye-opener*)?

If your answer is *yes* to two or more questions, then you should consider further assessment of your drinking behavior and the need to obtain assistance.

Another more detailed self-assessment test that you can take is called the Michigan Alcohol Screening Test that is available online at: *counselingresource.com/quizzes/alcohol-mast/index.html*

If you wish to compare your drinking pattern with others visit: *www.drinkerscheckup.com* or *www.rethinkdrinking.niaaa.nih.gov*

Fill out these *checkups* when you have a chance. You do *not* have to report your scores to anyone. It is for your own information.

Here are some additional signs that alcohol or drug use is becoming a problem:

• You feel guilty about your alcohol or drug use.

• Your family or friends comment on how much you are drinking.

- Your drinking or drug use makes it hard to live up to your responsibilities at home or at work.

- You need more alcohol or drugs to get the same effect.

- You have tried to cut down on your own, but can't.

- You have not been able to cut down or stop.

- You have not been able to stick to drinking limits.

- You have shown signs of withdrawal such as tremors, sweating, nausea, and insomnia.

- You spent a lot of time drinking or using drugs or planning on ways to obtain substances.

- You have had relationship problems, role failures and run-ins with the law because of alcohol or drug use.

- You have engaged in risky behaviors like driving, swimming, using dangerous equipment while under the influence of alcohol or drugs.

If your answers to these *Hinge Questions* are "yes," you should consider what *triggers* your drinking in terms of people (who are you with), places (where are you) and activities (what are you doing). Help is available. To read stories of individuals ("recovery heroes") who have successfully quit various forms of addiction visit *www.quitandrecovery.org*.

Additional resources that may be of assistance in helping individuals who have substance abuse problems include Alcoholic Anonymous and Smart Recovery which provide peer-to-peer supports. For instance, see the following websites.

About.com at *alcoholism.about.com/od/meetings/a/ann-e_app.htm*

SMART Recovery at *www.smartrecovery.com*

National Institute on Alcohol Abuse and Alcoholism at *www.niaaa.nih.gov*

Safe Drinking Tips

- Set drinking limits for yourself and stick to them.

- Drink slowly. Have no more than two drinks in any three hours.

- For every drink of alcohol, have one or more non-alcoholic drinks.

- Eat before and while you are drinking.

- Reduce your long-term health risks for men by drinking no more than 15 drinks per week, with no more than three drinks per day, most days, and for women, 10 drinks per week with no more than two drinks a day, most days.

Quotable Quotes

The newspaper headline read 'Alcoholism, bankruptcy beset super-agent' and went on to detail the journey of Leigh Steinberg, the model character for Tom Cruise's portrayal of Jerry Maguire. Steinberg who has now been sober for two years observes:

> *"I am an alcoholic today and will be for the rest of my life. I don't want anyone else to go through the pain and denial that I did. You only live this life once. I still think I can be of service." (USA Today February 21, 2012, David Leon Moore)*

ACTION #6

I need to use productive health-engendering ways to cope with physical and emotional pain and stress, instead of self-destructive coping tools such as alcohol and non-prescribed drugs.

Useful Information

Imagine therapy that had no known side effects, was readily available, and could improve your cognitive functioning at zero costs. Such a therapy has been known to philosophers, writers, and laypeople alike: interacting with nature.

Nature heals and improves cognitive functioning, reduces mental chatter and negative thinking, calms, reminds one of what is really important in life and enhances overall well-being. Nature can be restorative—sounds of silence and the exposure to natural sights, sounds and smells.

Quotable Quotes

> *"Going on Outward Bound adventures, in nature, with fellow vets, was a healing journey."*

> *"Being out at sea is a time for reflection."*

> *"The transition back is difficult, especially for young vets, being in nature; undertaking challenging tasks like kayaking the rapids, mountain climbing, hiking with my battle buddies helped a lot."*

ACTION #7

I should avoid high-risk dangerous sensation-seeking behaviors such as driving aggressively or recklessly or what are called "chasing adrenaline-rush behaviors."

Another form of high-risk behavior is engaging in uncontrollable gambling. Visit the website *www.gamblersanonymous.com* and the 20 question self-assessment test to determine if gambling behaviors are problematic for you and what productive steps you can take (call 1-888-GA-HELPS).

Useful Information

Some forms of sensation-seeking behaviors have been found to *bolster* resilience. For example, an organization Paralyzed Veterans of America (www.pva.org) have created thrill seeking extreme sport activities such as hang gliding, mountain climbing and downhill skiing, as a means to therapeutically challenge and engage paralyzed service members in relatively safe supervised adrenaline-charged activities. Thus, sensation-seeking behaviors can be *both* a risk factor (e.g., riding motorcycles without helmets) or a protective resilience-enhancing factor.

As an example of *risks*, consider the findings that *traffic accidents* are the leading cause of death for military personnel in their first year home from the war. More veterans die from car accidents than from suicide. The service members dying tend to be young, unmarried males. They tend to come from the infantry ranks, or gun crews or in seamanship roles. Iraq and Afghanistan veterans are 75% more likely to die in car accidents than the general population.

Veterans engage in more risky behaviors—speeding, alcohol, not wearing seat belts, or not wearing motorcycle helmets. These veterans are trained to drive aggressively while in combat and in a hyper vigilant manner. They may employ driving techniques taught in Iraq such as speeding up at intersections to avoid gunfire or scanning the roadside for danger instead of watching the road ahead or driving through stop signs.

A recent survey indicated that while deployed 50% said they were anxious when other cars approached quickly, 23% had driven through stop signs, and 20% were anxious during normal driving. These driving habits carry over during post-deployment and put them at risk. Moreover, they may think they are "invincible." They have gone through combat and they may believe that "they can live through anything." In addition, the conditions of PTSD and traumatic brain injuries could contribute to erratic and risky driving, as well as the use of medications and self-medications (using alcohol or illegal drugs) to cope with symptoms. A Safe Driving Training program has now begun to increase veterans and family members' awareness of driving accidents, to encourage use of seat belts, and re-train drivers and to identify where additional help is needed. Driving retraining programs teach service members how to regain composure by training them to identify those things that make them anxious and learning how to use Tactical Breathing Procedures (See Action #41) and Self-talk Procedures (Action #42).

ACTION #8

Here are other examples of my *wellness tools* and ways that I can improve my *physical fitness*. (Please e-mail these suggestions to *examples@roadmaptoresilience.org*)

_____

_____

_____

_____

Interpersonal Fitness

"Good social relationships are associated with enhanced happiness, increased cognitive capacity, improved quality of life and greater resilience."

"Resiliency is rooted in and rests fundamentally on relationships, both the perceived and actually received amount and quality of social supports."

"Psychological health involves people needing to feel connected and having a sense of belongingness."

"Individuals who feel lonely and socially isolated are prone to poorer health, compromised immune systems, cardiac diseases, and early death. Social interactions can produce changes in the experience and biology of loneliness."

"When you do not have hope, you can look for it in the face of a friend or loved one."

"Avoid isolation: It is easier to find courage when I am not alone."

Interpersonal fitness is the capacity to foster, engage in and sustain positive relationships and to endure and recover from life stressors with the assistance and support of others. Socially resilient individuals evidence the willingness to both ask for help and offer help when needed and build mutually caring relationships.

This section will provide practical suggestions on how to improve your relationships by:

a) fine-tuning your communication skills
b) learning ways to handle interpersonal conflicts more effectively
c) learning ways to nurture your relationship with a partner/spouse
d) developing ways to reenter, reengage, reconnect, reintegrate and become more *resilient*

ACTION #9

I need to recognize that deployment changes everyone, both warriors and family members, and recognize that there is a difference between military life and civilian life. Readjustment and overcoming the *disconnect* takes time.

I should recognize that civilian life does not follow the same rules as military life, such as respect for authority, discipline and camaraderie. There is a need to *renegotiate* my role at home. As my GPS system always reminds me when I am lost, *recalibrating*.

Useful Information

Many of the things service members learned in the military served them well while deployed or while in a combat zone. But, some of those same strategies and skills may be causing difficulties in their civilian roles. What worked over there may *not* work back home. It is a "Stuckness" problem.

Perhaps this adjustment challenge was best captured by Chaplain Douglas Etter* who offered the following observations about his experience of coming home.

- For 18 months, I was surrounded by men with guns. When I came home I felt vulnerable without them, even in church.

- For 18 months, I suffered the indignities and deprivations of military life in a combat environment with a core of friends. When I came home I felt lonely without them, even when surrounded by family or other friends.

- For 18 months, I kept a constant watch on my surroundings and the people all around me. When I returned home, I could not break the habit, but remained hyper vigilant outside the walls of my home.

- For 18 months, I studied every piece of garbage or discarded junk along the road. When I came home, I couldn't stop. Riding in the passenger's seat always made me nervous when someone would drive over a piece of trash.

- For 18 months as a leader of soldiers, I had to keep my emotions in check. When I came home, people told me I was distant and withdrawn.

- For 18 months, I shared common goals with others with whom I depended literally for my life. When I came home, I found dishonesty, hypocrisy and malevolence in people who claimed to be my friends and share common values.

- For 18 months, I had no choice about what to wear, what to eat, what to do or when to sleep. When I came home, I was overwhelmed by choices, sometimes to the point that I was unable to make decisions.

- For 18 months, I dealt with issues that were literally life and death, one's eternal in their scope. When I returned home, I found people worried about matters of no consequence at all.

* [Reprinted with permission by the Institue for Research, Education & Training in Addictions (www.IRETA.org)]

For further examples of the transitional stressors of shifting from military to civilian life visit the following website *www.realwarrirors.net*. "Battlemind" skills helped you survive in combat, but they can cause you problems if not adapted when you get home.

Quotable Quotes

"I understand that it took time to train myself for my mission as a warrior, and I must allow myself time to readjust feeling like a civilian again."

"When I first returned from combat I felt like a stranger at home. My son had grown up so much and had really become independent. My wife was running my house and doing well at it. I felt that I had missed a lot with birthdays, anniversaries, holidays and school activities. I had a pretty easy transition because I was able to take my time and slip back into my role in the family. We haven't encountered any major issues. We all became more mature people with the separation."

"My transition to civilian life has been weird. My wife tells me I changed and that I have a shorter fuse. She tells me that I make rash decisions. I can't stand stupid people. I use to get pissed off when she told me this and then I thought maybe she is right. Now I can catch myself and step back. Actually, I think I have matured as a result of my deployment. I can now appreciate my family and friends more if I just take the time. It just takes time and some deliberate practice."

ACTION #10

I need to stay connected (not isolate, avoid, detach myself from others), recognize that I am not alone and reconnect with social supports, even if it is difficult at first. If I am an officer or NCO, I can check in with my soldiers and provide support.

Studies of military families reveal that the factor that most strongly influenced the unit's readiness and retention was the amount of perceived support given to the family by the unit and the commanders. Leaders who highly prioritized morale, had units that functioned better and were more prepared and resilient, compared with leaders who highly prioritized discipline. Perceived family support is central to the morale, stability and resilience of the individual service member. Good leaders make an effort to know their warriors and their families.

Check on the quality of your relationships and supports by *honestly* answering the following *Hinge Questions*.

- "Who can I turn to for social supports?" List family members, friends, war buddies, co-workers, others?"

- "Who are the family members and friends who are helpful? In what ways are they helpful?"

- "Do I have at least one friend who I feel close to?"

- "How often do I feel part of a group?"

- "Whom can I turn to in times of crisis?"

- "What usually happens when I ask for support from family and friends?"

- "What can I do to improve the situation so I receive more support?"

- "What do I do to provide support?" (Remember I have to give to get).

- "Do I have close relationships with people who have a *positive influence* on my life? If not, what can I do to develop such relationships?"

- "Are there people I need to avoid when I am feeling distressed (uptight, bored, agitated, depressed)?"

- "Do I have the strategies, abilities, confidence and desire to cope with *unhealthy, harmful* relationships? If not, what can I do to protect myself?"

- "How have I handled conflicts in my life? What has worked for me that I can use now?"

I need to remember that "coming home from deployment can be like *emigrating* to a new land and I need to build a new life within a new culture from the one I left behind, as I move from the War Zone to the Home Zone."

For assistance, I can go to the following websites:
www.guardfamily.org
www.militaryonesource.com
www.jointservicesupport.org
and for family and couple supports:
Search RFSMC on *www.usuhs.mil/*
(See Action #81 for a list of additional websites)

ACTION #11

I should lean on others. Seek and accept
    a. Gifts of the Heart (emotional social supports)
    b. Gifts of the Hands (practical, tangible helping actions)
    c. Gifts of the Head (informational guidance and advice)

Some individuals have difficulty determining if they, indeed, have problems that warrant seeking help. One strategy that has been used successfully with traumatized individuals is to have them fill out the following Self-assessment Worksheet that was developed by Dr. Ronald Murphy with his clients. What problems, if any, do you have that you can work on? Filling out the chart honestly will help you assess your life situation.

Problem Identification Worksheet

If you look at your life, you can take stock of which category problem areas such as anger, intimacy, isolation, trust, legal, health, sleep, alcohol, smoking and being a perfectionist fall under. Has someone you care about urged you to get help for these problems? Have you felt guilty or embarrassed about the way you handled this situation? Has an important relationship at home, at work, or among friends been strained because of this problem? Do you feel you need to seek assistance? What might get in the way of your seeking such help?

Problems I definitely have:
Problems I wonder if I have:
Problems other people say I have:
Problems I definitely don't have:

Quotable Quotes

"When I took stock, I realized I need help. I needed to change how I was spending my time."

"When I went back to college, I discovered how many other vets were fellow students. I was able to hook up with them. It brought back my sense of belonging, connectedness. I was able to lean on them for information (head support), shared story-telling (heart support) and car pooling (hand support)."

ACTION #12

I must give back and help others, have a friend and be a friend, help others in order to expand the circle of people I can call upon in difficult times. Reducing the suffering of others can help create a sense of meaning and personal growth.

Useful Information

The Dalai Lama observed that one should be *wise selfish* by which he was highlighting that the best way to help yourself is by helping others. Love and service to others bring rewards to oneself that otherwise would be unachievable."

In their book *Why Good Things Happen to Good People*, Stephen Post, Jill Neimark and Otis Moss observe: "Giving is the most potent force in the planet and will protect you your whole life."

Being altruistic reduces unhealthy qualities like stress, greed, jealousy and self-centeredness while fostering qualities such as happiness, mental health, well-being and a sense meaning/purpose to life. People who volunteer to help others are physically healthier and even live longer. Spending one's time and resources on others can contribute to what is called a "helper's high". Moreover, such "give back" can have a "multiplier effect" and ripple through a social network and induce cooperation and altruism in others.

Please answer the following *Hinge Questions*.

Can you recall an instance of altruism that you received from someone else? Can you recall a memory of altruism that you shared with someone else?

Consider what gifts you can share with others. As Dr. Robert Brooks (Brooks & Goldstein, 2003) observes, we are not talking about material gifts like money or material objects, but your *personal gifts* or *island of competence* that you possess that you can share with others.

Gifts are abilities that we are born with and can develop. We each have an *island of competence* or an area that is or has the potential to be a source of pride and achievement that we can share with others.

- "What 'island of competence' do I have?"

- "What abilities and positive qualities do I have?"

- "What positive qualities do people say I have?"

- "How would I like others to describe me?"

- "How would they actually describe me?"

- "If there is a difference between how I would like others to describe me and how they would actually describe me, what steps can I take so that they will describe me in the way I would like?"

- "Would I want anyone to say or do to me what I have done to others?"

- "Who are the people in my life that I can give to?"

- "When was the last time that I shared with someone else? What was it?"

- "What do I give that makes me feel good?"

- "Give a recent example of when you were an affectionate/agree-able/attentive listener; considerate/compassionate/empathetic/fun to be with/forgiving/generous/ respectful/responsive to the needs of others; supportive/trustworthy."

- "What examples would love ones and friends offer of each of these behaviors that they have seen you demonstrate?"

Quotable Quotes

"No act of kindness, no matter how small is ever wasted."

"Stress is cumulative. It can pile up. I had to detox for a few hours. I had to find someone to share this with. If I felt alone, if I felt that the Army did not acknowledge my sacrifice, it made it worse. The Army preaches, the Band of Brother's concept: 'Leave no man behind.' This applies while bullets are flying during combat and it also applies after a deployment when soldiers are wrestling with the memories of the war. We are expected to stand by each other.

It also applies to my family who had to live through my deployment. Remember TO GIVE IS TO GET."

"I had a Battle Buddy. Now I have a Family Buddy."

ACTION #13

I need to participate in a supportive social network and stay involved in social settings such as church, community activities, and sports-related activities. I should hang around with people who value joy and improve the situation and who are on a meaning-making mission. I need to participate in *communal coping efforts* that generate a sense of hope, trust, solidarity, and connectedness such as public rituals, memorials, demonstrations, marches, artistic expressive activities, theatre performances, reconciliation meetings, religious services, and the like. *Find a way to matter to other people.*

Useful Information

People with five or more close friends (excluding family members) are 50 percent more likely to describe themselves as being "very happy," than folks who had few friends. One in four Americans reports they have no one to confide in. It takes effort and commitment to find and maintain a confidant, but it is critical to the development of resilience.

Quotable Quotes

"Over time, I learned to deal with my anger by placing emotional distance between myself and the Army. The Army is still an important part of my life, but I make a conscious effort now not to let it control my life. I set firm boundaries with the military—not working past a certain hour, living off post, respecting my wife's wish not to participate in unit functions. In the Army's place I now focus my energy on the things that make the most sense to me in my life- my family, my friends and my travels."
—Major Andrew J. Dekever, Notre Dame Magazine, Autumn, 2011

ACTION #14

I need to share my emotions with someone I trust and tell them what I am going through. The recognition and disclosure of the nature of the traumatic event is fundamental to recovery. Talk about my war time experiences at a time when I think it is right to do so and with an understanding and sympathetic person (family member, friend, fellow soldier, battle buddy, Chaplain, counselor). I can decide how much I share and what to say.

Useful Information

Soldiers who had spoken about their experiences were less distressed than those who had not shared their combat experiences with a trusted person.

When individuals who had been abused in childhood were asked what was most helpful in dealing with the abuse and its aftermath, what were the turning points in their lives, they reported experiences with others where they felt genuine acceptance, felt loved and nurtured and had a sense of belonging and connection.

Individuals who do *not* share what they experienced and clam up and keep secrets have a much more difficult time adjusting. This does *not* mean that they have to re-experience or go into detail. They can use "broad brush strokes," instead of going into "nitty gritty" details which works well in facilitating shifts in thinking and feeling. Some individuals do quite well without reliving and revisiting memories of what they experienced. The critical point is that it is a "sign of strength" to have the courage to share with supportive others at *one's own pace. Remember: what cannot be talked about cannot be put to rest.*

Quotable Quotes

"Talking to others after the trauma is the mind's way of healing itself."

"I need to talk to someone who can listen attentively, in a nonjudgmental fashion, who can offer appropriate practical advice, and who can provide practical help when necessary."

"Like hands shaping a piece of modeling clay, conversation transforms the meanings that we make of our experiences."

"Through conversation, I gain new perspectives, correct misconceptions and find new insights and can focus on the positives."

"I had to learn who I can confide in, what was appropriate to share and when to hold back."

ACTION #15

How To: Improve My Communication (Listening and Speaking) Skills

In terms of *Listening Skills* I can:

> A—Attend with genuine interest to what the other person is saying. Ask open-ended questions to better understand my partner's point of view.

For example, ask "What" and "How" questions of my partner. ("*What* did you mean when you said X?"; "*How* did you come to the decision to do Y? Walk me through the steps.") *be curious, not furious* with any actions and comments your spouse makes.

B—**B**e responsive to what is said.

C—**C**are about the other person and accept his/her perspective. Try to figure out what the person might be thinking and feeling.

D—**D**o *not* interrupt my partner and do not finish my partner's sentences, but instead wait until he/she is finished. Then say or do something to show that I understand the person's perspective.

E—**E**ncourage the person to say more and to feel safe, speaking to me as a confidant. Ask the other person if what I did or said helped and made the person feel understood. Watch for reactions to my behavior and what I said and how I said it and respond appropriately to the person's reactions. If what I said or did, or did not say or did not do had a negative impact, apologize and reword what I was trying to say. Think about what would be the best way to convey what I want or feel. What are the best words and tone of voice to use? Ask myself, if someone said or did the same thing to me, how I would feel?

In addition, I can learn to:

Actively listen—by putting my best *ear* forward. Listen to not only what is being said, but how it is being said. Listen for the meaning behind the words and check it out. Ask myself, "What am I missing?"

Parrot back—simply repeat back verbatim or restate what my partner has said and raise any questions of clarification.

Paraphrase—rephrase in my own words the content of the communication. Tell my partner what I got out what he/she said.

Reflect—figure out the emotion behind the speaker's message and check it out. Accept and show greater emotional understanding of one another.

Show Empathy—convey to the speaker that his/her perspective is understandable. Say or do something that my loved one needs from me right now (a kind word, a hug). Appreciate that my partner's response to me may be influenced by the history, back-story or "baggage" that he/she brings to the relationship. Don't forget to maintain perspective and consider the *big picture.* Empathy says to my partner that he/she is being heard and valued.

In terms of *Speaker's Skills*, I can learn new ways of talking.

Be clear and brief—in what I say. Refer to specific behaviors.

Be positive—Use non-accusatory, understanding statements. Use "I" statements, instead of "you" attacking statements. For example, I can say:

"I feel ___ when you do ___ in situations such as ___ because ___."

"I feel (embarrassed, uncomfortable, unsafe) when you (criticize me, use your loud voice and become angry) in (front of company, when we are driving) because (I cannot predict how you will respond; the argument might escalate.)"

"I feel (appreciated, understood, loved) when you give me a (hug, say kind things, share your feelings) when (we are alone, with my parents) because I feel (valued, understood.")

People listen more effectively and respond in a reciprocal manner when they receive such positive statements. In contrast, when I use "You" statements such as:

"You only . . . "

"I feel that you . . . , or use blaming or blackmailing statements such as: "If you don't X, I will Y."\

"You (*always, never*) statements" which are rarely accurate and contribute to communication breakdowns.

"You" statements are perceived as accusatory and threatening and contribute to interpersonal distress.

Edit—what I say. I do not have to say every thought I have. Each thought is not a commandment to speak or act.

Exert behavioral control—I can say what I think and feel without putting others down or putting them at risk for physical or emotional harm. Body language counts. It is not only what I say, but how I say it.

Perspective take—check out if my message has been heard as intended.

Share—I can ask my spouse/partner for what I need/want in a supportive way and I can ask my spouse/partner what he/she needs/wants in a supportive way.

Problem-solve with my partner - -Together we can set collaborative *goals*, make *plans, do* them and *check* to see how they work—*goal, plan, do, check.*

ACTION #16

How To: be a Good Social Problem Solver

(Keep in mind these are recommendations, not rigid rules to be followed.)

1. Work together with my partner to identify and understand the problematic situation, "What is bothering the two of us?"

2. Describe the specific behaviors that are occurring or not occurring objectively and check out my view of the situation with the other person.

3. Express one idea and then stop and allow my partner to respond.

4. Ask the other person for his/her perspective.

5. Try to see things from their perspective.

6. Together work to break down "big" problems into smaller problems and deal with each problem separately. Chunk the problems and prioritize them, together.

7. Do not dwell on the past or try to blame each other. Focus on right now and the future.

8. Consider brainstorming (considering as many options as possible) in order to increase the number of alternatives.

9. Negotiate and compromise in formulating possible solutions that should be stated in clear behavioral terms.

10. Allow for several attempts at implementing the new solutions.

11. Discuss the benefits to the relationship when changes have been made.

12. Set aside a time and a place to have such social problem-solving conversations.

ACTION #17

How To: Improve My Conflict Management Skills

In all relationships, it is inevitable that some form of disagreements and conflicts will emerge. How couples and families handle and resolve such conflicts influence their abilities to become resilient, especially in the aftermath of traumatic and victimizing experiences.

How To: Handle Inevitable Conflicts with Your Partner or Spouse

1. Do *not* avoid conflicts with your partner/spouse, but instead deal with the conflict constructively and cooperatively. Create a sense of trust and safety.

2. Avoid attack-defend and demand-withdrawal modes of communicating that contribute to marital conflict and dissatisfaction. Demand by one partner can be met by withdrawal by the other partner. The "withdrawer" might change the topic, focus on some other perceived inadequacy of the "demander" as a way of avoiding the central topic or just give in. ("Sometimes, I just give in or withdraw from the conversation because I love her and I do not want to lose control and say or do something that will hurt her.")

3. Do *not* use sullen silence, withdrawal, accusatory statements to resolve or avoid conflicted issues. There is a need to recognize such communication patterns early on and catch and change them.

4. When arguing do not bring up "ancient history." Stay focused on the present and the immediate future, not in the past. Leave the past in the past. Identify specific things you can do differently in the present and tell your partner how you intend to change.

5. Express your requests *positively*, instead of negatively. Instead of saying:

    > "I do *not* like it when you say/do X."
    > *instead*
    > "I prefer it when you say/do Y."

    > "I do *not* want you to do Z."
    > *instead*
    > "I would like you to (greatly appreciate, be most grateful to you) for saying/doing Z."

    Think about how you would like to be asked to do something. Craft your words carefully. Remember that words spoken in anger cannot be unspoken.

6. Understand that happily married couples say *five positive remarks* for every negative remark, even when having conflicts. Couples headed for divorce use less than one (0.8) positive remarks for every negative remark.

7. Look for the complexity of an issue. View the topic of conflict from your partner's/spouse's perspective. Surrender the notion that you know all the answers. Focus on "we" and not just on "me."

8. Develop a warning system with your partner that you are angry about something, but not quite ready to talk about it. For example, light a special candle that can be used only for this purpose. This is a signal that you need to cool down and then discuss the topic when cooler heads prevail. ("When I get emotionally flooded, it is almost impossible to have a productive conversation with my partner"). Keep in mind that hyper arousal is most strongly associated with aggressive behavior, especially when co-occurring with alcohol abuse. Keep conflicts civil and calm.

9. If the conflict gets heated, take a *time out* if you feel it necessary, from the argument. Allow your emotions to subside. Then call *time in*.

10. Never let the sun go down with anger still lingering within you. Anger magnifies and amplifies the negative aspects of the issue. Such "smoldering feelings" undermine relationships and blocks the development of resilience. (See Action #15, #16, and #41 for a discussion of ways to manage anger and hostility).

11. Repair any regrettable incidents in your relationships. Take responsibility for your part in the conflict. Avoid blaming. Upon reflection, indicate what you have learned from this conflicted situation and what you intend to do specifically to improve your relationship.

Start fresh each morning.

ACTION #18

How To: Nurture My Relationship with my Partner or Spouse

An investment in a relationship is like any other investment. You get out of it what you put into it. In order to profit and reap dividends, you need to watch over the relationship and care for it. Avoidance and numbing reactions to trauma are most strongly associated with problems in family and intimate relationship functioning. Here are some specific steps you and your partner/spouse can take *together* to nurture your relationship.

1. To begin, never forget what attracted you to your partner in the first place. Remember together how you got together in the first place and hooked up or got married. Together you can go through picture albums and recall the shared happy and good times together and how you can maintain and recreate those same feelings and experiences. Take time to get to know each other all over again. Think of times when you felt close, happy and got along well with each other.

2. Your communication (both verbal and nonverbal) with your partner/spouse should include a ratio of four to five positive to every negative statement.

Each instance of criticism, put downs, slights and the like, warrant at least four times as many positive interactions (positive attention, interest, expressions of appreciation, empathetic listening, humorous comments, and the like). You have to actively work to reduce the level of negativity of criticism, defensiveness, contempt and stonewalling (refusal to cooperate and comply).

3. There is a need for *both* partners to recognize the rigid "vicious cycle" or pattern of communication that leads to "gridlock" and "escalation." There is a need to recognize when the two of you are falling into this "communication trap" and learn ways to notice this pattern early on to interrupt and override it. Instead of fueling the "cycle," the two of you can view the "cycle" as an "enemy" that needs to be avoided and defeated. Instead of blaming each other, blame the "cycle" and work together to change it, before it destroys your relationship. Learn to stand together against this destructive process. You can work together to alter the "dance of disconnection." Work with your new battle-buddy, your partner, like you worked with your war buddies.

4. Remember that reducing negativity is necessary, but *not sufficient* for a successful relationship. *Positivity needs to be increased*, particularly during conflict situations. Compassion, affection, humor, honoring the other's life dreams need to be part of any communication. Any bids for attention and affection should be met with a reciprocal response ("turn toward bids"). Talk about shared goals, missions and legacies. Express appreciation and admiration of your partner/spouse each day. Be specific and provide detailed examples. (*You are so creative in making our home decorative for the holidays, of putting together a romantic dinner, of supporting your friends*). Comment on what you like, enjoy and appreciate about your partner/spouse. Praise each other's efforts, not just the outcomes.

5. Use the *language of solutions* and the *language of becoming* with your partner/spouse that notices, acknowledges and highlights ways your partner is changing. (*You are becoming more—supportive, caring, loving when you—* provide specific examples). Catch each other doing nice things and praise such behaviors.

6. Write a letter of gratitude ("thank you") to your partner/spouse expressing your appreciation for something he/she has done for you or the family. Be specific and write down how it affected you. Read the letter aloud to your partner/spouse. Offer a kind word or flowers. Offer a hug or a massage.

7. Be emotionally generous. Engage in acts of kindness, fondness, and share responsibilities. Surprise your partner/spouse with something fun and romantic. Target marital friendship, exchanges of positive feelings and *joint* meaningful goals and missions.

8. (Re) negotiate and (re) establish routines, responsibilities and rules for the family so you do not feel like a "guest in your home." Work together to

"shrink" the impact of stress and any lingering effects of deployment, traumatic events and victimizing experiences. Work *together* to *gradually* approach and overcome any avoidance behaviors that resulted in the aftermath of traumatic events. With your partner's/spouse's assistance break the habit of reducing distress through avoidance. Create a hierarchy of situations and activities that are avoided from least fearful to most fearful. Work together to overcome them gradually (confront, enter, engage in), these avoidant behaviors, from least to most anxiety-engendering. Work as a *team*.

9. Share difficult experiences and accompanying feelings. Doing so is the "emotional glue" that cements social bonds. Turn toward each other, instead of away or apart. Nurture a sense of togetherness, instead of withdrawing.

10. Be careful of one's partner "running interference" by over-protecting the other partner. In a desire to help the distressed partner, a spouse may make excuses; cover for him/her; do for his/her spouse what he/she should be doing for him/herself; assume that it is his/her job to fix problems for the partner. Such *enabling behaviors* can inadvertently reinforce avoidance behaviors. A spouse can become a *Surrogate Frontal Lobe* for a distressed partner and take on planning, organizing, monitoring functions. There is a need for partners/spouses to be partners, asking each other how he/she can be of assistance.

11. Make a list with your spouse of activities you both like to do together and do the top ones. Schedule enjoyable positive "healthy" activities and events, like a scheduled date outside of the home at least once a month. Have fun. Show affection, permit intimacy to (re) develop. Find ways to be close that do not involve sex, such as sharing affection in other ways. Spend quality time together.

12. Behaviors that can *undermine* relationships. Do the ***opposite*** of these behaviors.

    a. Act as if you are superior and know all the answers and speak to your partner in a condescending and *contemptible tone*.

    b. Be defensive and respond angrily to criticism by counter-attacking, crying, or employing the silent treatment in an attempt to punish the other person.

    c. Convey that certain topics are "taboo" to discuss. "Stonewall" and "filibuster." Withdraw physically or emotionally from the discussion. Say, "okay, okay, I will do it your way."

    d. Contradict any positive statements you offer your partner by pairing them with *nonverbal negative* messages such as frowns, sneers, expressions of disgust; use a tense and impatient tone of voice, lean away from your partner, and the like. Send two conflicting messages. *Remember that looks can speak louder than words.*

e. Control everything and everyone. Be a "control freak." Convey the belief that "If you loved me, you would know what I want and need."

f. Find fault with your partner. Let days go by without a kind word or a loving gesture.

g. Pay more attention to your TV or computer than to your partner.

h. Strike the words "I love you" from your vocabulary.

i. Never let your partner see you smiling.

j. Never ask your partner for help.

k. Keep your feelings to yourself.

l. Withdraw sex and let passion die (you get extra points for this one).

(Suggestions offered above by Pat Love and Sunny Shulkin in their tongue-in-cheek book, *How to Ruin a Perfectly Good Relationship.* Do not forget to do the opposite of these if you want to nurture a good relationship.)

13. Visit couple-based websites, workshops, references or a spouse battlemind program. For example:
    www.resilience.army.mil/
    www.strongbonds.org
    www.spousonomics.com
    www.couplescoachingcouples.com

See also John Gottman's books *The Seven Principles for Making Marriage Work; The Relationship Cure;* and *Why Marriages Succeed or Fail.* Also Susan Johnson's *Hold Me Tight* and Howard Markman, Scott Stanley and Susan Blumberg's *Fighting For Your Marriage.*

Quotable Quotes

"I can let my spouse know when I am struggling so she can become more patient and supportive."

"I can let my guard down. I do not have to put up a wall. Instead of shutting down I can let my spouse in."

"We have both learned to slow down the whole interaction cycle before responding to each other."

"As a result our conflicts have decreased. I am a better listener. It brought us together."

"I have learned to share my fears and ask for help."

"Our communications are more open and effective."

"I have a greater appreciation of what my spouse is going through ('echoes of battle') and its lingering effects."

"I feel more trust in my spouse."

"I really feel like part of a team with my spouse."

ACTION #19

I can overcome barriers to seeking help, such as fear of stigma, feelings of distrust, and concerns about what others will think about my seeking help. Get help from peers, Chaplain, mental health counsellors. Such "expert companionship" provides an opportunity for self-disclosure and consideration of various perspectives on the current stressors and experiences. Such assistance has proven effective in helping individuals, couples and communities find peace and achieve growth. For a humorous discussion of ways to seek help, visit *mantherapy.org*.

Useful Information

Consider some of the concerns that returning service members may have that get in the way of their asking for help. Do you have any of these concerns and how can they be addressed?

1. Concerns about "stigma" for getting help

    "What will others—my buddies, commander, and family members--think of me if they learn that I am going for help?"

    "Going for help would be embarrassing." "I would be open to ridicule."

2. Concerns about the possible consequences of getting help

    "If I go for help it might get out and jeopardize my military career or further assignments or delay my family reunion or risk my job."

    "Members of my unit might have less confidence in me."

    "My commander may blame me for the problem."

    "I would be seen as being weak."

3. Concerns about the effectiveness of treatment

   "I do not think they will understand me."

   "Treatment may make me worse, dredging up all those war stories."

   "Counselling will bring back so many intense reminders of events in combat that I am deliberately trying to forget."

   "I will get better on my own—time will heal things."

4. Concerns about getting help do not fit with how I see myself.

   "I am supposed to be a warrior and I need to suck it up and drive on."

   "I feel ashamed for being troubled by my military experiences."

   "I learned to ignore my feelings."

   "I am not supposed to feel emotions other than anger."

   "I might cry and that is unacceptable. Crying shows weakness that can get you dead. Becoming emotional is a distraction and makes you vulnerable. If you are distracted you can lose focus and in the world that I lived in that means someone might die."

   "To be a man you are supposed to ignore or deny pain, especially emotional pain."

5. Concerns about the information I am receiving.

   "I avoid such information because it:

      "leads to unpleasant feelings"

      "might demand undesired changes or actions"

      "threatens my cherished beliefs about myself."

See *www.MakeTheConnection.net/Stories-of-Connection* for stories of the benefits of service members getting help. Listen for the ways they handle and overcome each of these concerns.

Additional barriers to help-seeking include concerns about *secrecy* ("what goes on in the house stays in the house"), *stoicism* (maintain a public face of stability and the ability to handle any stressors"; "putting on a good face") and *denial* ("keep all feelings, fears, family issues under wraps" and "not to be shared"). Avoiding, suppressing, clamming up, delaying to seek help, all have the potential of making things worse. There are effective treatments and many service members have benefited. Consider the following observations of the *benefits of treatment*.

Quotable Quotes

"Remember, it takes the courage and strength of a warrior to ask for help."

"Courage is the ability to face adversity, even if it is within yourself."

"It is impressive what you can achieve just by sharing and owning your own story. It is all about sharing."

"It is your call, but remember, veterans are getting treatment every day."

"I can go for help not only for me, but for those I love and care for."

"I know that if the troops I lost could talk to me right now, they would say, 'Come on, you are living for me now. Pick up your game.'"

"My commitment to taking care of my children gave me the reason to stop drinking."

"Treatment got me from rock bottom to living well. As a result of treatment I learned how to:
  "Recognize my triggers."
  "Let go of fear."
  "Calm down."
  "Free myself from negative thinking."
  "End the grip of nightmares and flashbacks."
  "Feel again and share my emotions, instead of keeping them buried."

"I used to drink to hide my pain and keep the shit out of my head."

"I used to take an 'internal retreat', securely wrapping myself in myself as a way to manage my fears. I'd remove myself from others, turning inward."

"I used to scan what everybody was doing. My brain just started working so fast and it is purely instinctual because I want to know what everyone's intent that is around me is. I want to know if anyone has the intent to do harm. Treatment taught me how not to be hyper vigilant."

"There is no shame for asking for help. No one can do this alone. I realize I am not the only one with these problems. You do not have to try and do it yourself."

"The more I talked, the more I made a connection and the more honest I became with myself. The stuff I did and witnessed left a scar on my soul. Talking about it helped. It acted like a release."

"It is amazing what you can do by just telling and owning your own story. It's all about talking."

"Taking the first step towards treatment was the most difficult. First, I had to acknowledge I had a problem and could not control how I was feeling. Treatment helped me develop the tools to handle my troublesome thoughts and feelings. With the help of my therapist, I was able to address many of the issues I battle in everyday life. I can now live a happy, healthy life, despite my experiences."

"Twenty-two years after his last combat experiences in World War II, America's best known hero, Audie Murphy, still slept with the lights on and with a loaded pistol by his bed. He couldn't bring himself to ask for help concerning his war stress. After all, he had been awarded the Congressional Medal of Honor."

"There was a time I would have called a soldier a weakling or worse for seeing a counsellor or going to a Chaplain. And if I didn't say it to his face, I sure would have thought it. I don't see it that way any more. Multiple deployments have taught me that we're all going to need help from time to time and it's the strong ones that are willing to ask for it."

"It was the Chaplain who made the difference. You know, just to talk about problems and issues in my life at that time, things I was struggling with. So he was very important to me, and I appreciated him because he was there for me. I was grateful I had someone to turn to."

"If it wasn't for my wife, I do not know where I would be right now, because she was always there for me."

"People notice things in me that I never noticed. Positive things I didn't know — they just helped me ground myself and they gave advice and support. They tell me when I'm ... well, they call me on my shit you know."

"Even though it was a hassle to get help, it was worth all the effort to persist and get help."

ACTION #20

Use community resources such as websites, volunteer organizations, telephone hotlines and social networks. Use my supportive *Circle of Friends*. (See Action #81 for list of Website resources).

Useful Information

Social isolation is associated with lower subjective well-being, poorer physical and emotional health and earlier death.

ACTION #21

Examples of Rituals

Use my cultural or ethnic traditions, rituals and identity as a support aide.

> *Reflection Activity*—close your eyes and reflect on the history of your people, especially those who have struggled. Get in touch with the strength of your heritage.

> Answer the following questions:

>> "I am, because we are . . . ?"
>> "Because we are, I am . . . ?"

> *Forgiveness Ceremony*—provide a "healing gift" to others and to yourself.

> *Rite of passage*—participate in a ceremonial transition ritual that helps the healing process. For example, attend a Native Sweat Lodge Activity; visit a memorial site; join a Soldier 2 Soldier activity.

> *Gift-giving Activity*—make a "gift" of your experience to others; convey lessons learned in order to promote other's well-being; use the wisdom of elders and those who have experience; learn from the coping skills of others.

ACTION #22

I can find a role model or mentor (real person or heroic figure) and let him/her act as a guide. Consider the following *Hinge Questions* about possible models and mentors in your life.

> "Do you know people who have gone through hard times and changed for the better?"

> "Do you read books or watch movies or television programs of people who have been exposed to traumatic events and who evidence resilience and post traumatic growth?"

> "What are the lessons you can learn from such individuals?"

Quotable Quotes

"The life of the Prophet Mohammad in the Quran brings solace and strength to many."

"I have thought a long time if this tragedy has also brought me anything positive, something special, something I never would have experienced without this experience. I noticed that I am surrounded by especially warm and loving people in my family and friends, people who really care about me and who support me and help whenever possible. I have learned who I can count on in times of extreme difficulties and sadness. But I also saw that I could count on myself. I did not let myself down."

"Studies of the wives of POWs (prisoners of war) find that they experienced both distress and growth compared to wives of Non-POW veterans. In the constant struggle with their husbands' difficulties, the wives of the POWs brought them closer and gave their lives meaning by putting them in a 'helper role'. Trauma affects those around the survivor, but by providing assistance, a sense of empowerment and personal growth is possible. The suffering of others may create a sense of growth in the helpers."

"When the pain of torture was overwhelming, I imagined vividly my mother in our garden. I could smell the grape leaves, touch the warm earth, and listen to her kind and reassuring voice. I imagined my playing my flute to her touching the invisible instrument with my fingers. These images brought me back to my senses. I used my consoling imagery to get through."

ACTION #23

I take pride in the camaraderie/friendship of my "Band of Brothers/Sisters" and the self-sacrifice and commitments I made for my Battle Buddies, unit, service and country. My "Band of Brothers/Sisters" is like family bonds that are formed under intense stress. Be proud of the mission we served.

Quotable Quotes

"I hold it to be one of the simplest truths of war that the thing which enables an infantry soldier to keep going with his weapons is the near presence or presumed presence of a comrade." —S.L. Marshall

"I remember the kind of combat flow where I was so absorbed in the present moment I lost all sense of time. This may sound crazy, but I felt more alive."

"While under heavy fire, an eerie sense of calm came over me. My mind was working with speed and clarity I would have found remarkable if I had time to reflect upon it. I knew what I was going to do. The whole plan of attack flashed through me in a matter of seconds."

"Within a year of returning home, I began growing nostalgic for the war . . . I could protest, but I could not deny the grip the war had on me, nor the fact that it had been an experience as fascinating as it was repulsive, as exhilarating as it was sad."

"The daily danger gave a zest to life that nothing else can give."—Philip Caputo in *A rumor of war.*

"I remember that I was a member of a resilient unit. We had good cohesion. High morale and caring leadership."

"I can bring these skills and attitudes back home with me and teach them to my kids."

"I can be part of my family unit, just like my combat unit—looking out for each other."

ACTION #24

Use a pet as a way to calm myself down, stay "grounded" and as a way to stay connected and meet new people. For example, there is a program that works with distressed veterans who have PTSD and trains these service members to teach dogs from shelters to befriend disabled veterans. (Operation Heroes and Hounds).

Quotable Quotes

"My pet terrier is trained to jump in my lap when it senses my distress. If my lap is not available, she will rub against my leg. I take her to work with me on some days. She helps me manage my moods."

ACTION #25

Here are other examples of ways I can improve my interpersonal fitness. (Please email these suggestions to *examples@roadmaptoresilience.org*)

_____

_____

_____

_____

Emotional Fitness

"Remember that emotions are normal, honorable and confirm your humanity."

"Emotions are sources of information; a signal worth listening to. They are relevance detectors and warning signs. Emotions tell us what we need and they can act as a guide."

"Most emotions are not wholly pleasant (positive) or wholly painful (negative), but rather a mixture of the two. Positive and negative emotions can co-exist."

"There is value in emotional pain such as compassion that can lead to helping others or in justified anger and indignation, grief, shame and guilt that can lead to taking positive actions."

"Negative emotions are necessary and not to be eliminated, but to be put to use. There is nothing wrong with negative emotions like anger, sadness, and anxiety. It is what one does with their emotions that is critical."

Emotional fitness is the ability to enhance positive emotions, self-regulate and transform negative emotions, and change one's relationship to emotions using acceptance strategies and mindfulness and meditative activities. Both positive and negative emotions can propel well-being and fuel *resilience*. They can provide a "sparkle of psychological glitter" and lead to enhanced compassion, and to positive actions.

This section will provide practical "how to" suggestions on ways to increase positive emotions and regulate negative emotions so as to bolster your *resilience*. Let's begin with ways of *increasing positive emotions*.

Useful Information

"Through experiences of positive emotions people transform themselves becoming more creative, knowledgeable, resilient, socially integrated and healthy individuals. We should work to cultivate positive emotions in ourselves and those around us as a means of achieving psychological growth and improve psychological and physical health." (B. Fredrickson, 2001)

Positive emotions can be intentionally self-generated and increased and they can *quiet* and *undo* the harmful effects of traumatic experiences and they can also *broaden* possible opportunities in life and *build upon* capacities and resources.

ACTION #26

I deliberately get active and (purposefully, intentionally, playfully) engage in pleasant activities that enhance my positive emotions and make me feel good (feelings of engagement, of interest, enthusiasm, joy, happiness, love, contentment, awe, curiosity, optimism, vitality, fulfillment, sense of mastery and self-confidence, pride, empathy, compassion, forgiveness and gratitude).

Useful Information

Repetitive experience of positive emotions can change the structure and function of the brain. More specifically, *positive emotions* can:

1. Dismantle or undo the effects of negative emotions and traumatic experiences.

2. Broaden visual attention, open individuals to new experiences and improve problem-solving abilities.

3. Propel a positive mindset of flexible thinking and trigger an upward emotional and behavioral spiral.

4. Ward off depression and reverse a downward negative emotional spiral of bad feelings rumination, worry, avoidance, withdrawal that becomes self-perpetuating.

5. Decrease threat appraisal and hyper vigilance.

6. Increase a sense of "oneness" with others and increase interpersonal trust.

7. Build and broaden coping skills and act as a buffer or bulwark against stressors in life.

8. Put things into perspective.

9. Tip the balance of the ratio of positive to negative feelings, thus opening up to new possibilities for change.

How To: Steps to Increase Positive Emotions

1. Ways to intentionally self-generate positive emotions:

a. Get involved in enjoyable activities. Remember that the word "recreation" is a "re-creation" and can contribute to a healthy lifestyle.

b. Increase pleasurable activities (hobbies, activities with loved ones and friends). Do something fun and engaging. Make the choice to be happy.

c. Emerge yourself in pleasurable aesthetic activities such as reading, music, art, enjoying nature (sunrises, sunsets), walks and the like. "Feed your soul!"

d. Anticipate and envision experiencing positive emotions.

e. Stretch yourself beyond previously established limits. Seek out and be open to new experiences. Develop new interests and look for new possibilities in life. Follow your curiosity.

f. Have hope which is the ability to produce pathways to attain goals. Engage in pathways thinking of positive courses of action.

g. Meaningfully engage with others on pleasurable activities. Savor joy. Increase social and emotional communication.

h. Repeat experiences that trigger positive emotions so they can become self-perpetuating "upward spirals." Capitalize on success.

2. *Tip the balance* of Positive to Negative Emotions to a 3 to 1 Ratio: 3 Positive to 1 Negative Emotion.

a. Employ positive mental imagery of past, present and future activities.

b. Recall positive past experiences and memories (go through picture albums with someone).

c. Reappraise past events. Look for the "silver lining." (Benefit finding and benefit remembering).

d. Focus on being in the present moment using mindfulness meditation which is a way to self-regulate your attention. In a non-evaluative manner attend to moment-by-moment experiences without fixating on thoughts of the past, nor the future. Positive emotions flow from the nonjudgmental focus on the present. Stay in the now. (See Action #41 for ways to conduct Mindfulness Activities).

e. Use acceptance strategies by changing my relationship with my thoughts. View my thoughts just as thoughts and not as directives or commandments to act or as truthful accounts. Come to accept my thoughts, memories and emotions without trying to needlessly change or alter them.

f. Engage in a "compassion" or "'loving- kindness" meditation and contemplation that reflects a warm and caring feeling toward self and others. (See Item 95 for ways to engage in compassion activities).

g. Do something soothing and relaxing (See Action #41 for ways to engage in relaxation and Tactical Breathing exercises).

h. Keep things in perspective. Remember my long-term goals and values.

i. Keep in mind that having fewer than 3-to-1 desirable-to-undesirable emotions is harmful for well-being. It is also harmful to have more than about 11-to-1 desirable-to-undesirable emotions. Balance is the key to the development and maintenance of resilience and well-being.

Quotable Quotes

As experts John Briere and Catherine Scott in trauma therapy observe:

> *"The implication is not that someone is 'lucky' when bad things happen, but rather, that not all outcomes associated with adversity are inevitably negative. The message is not that one should 'look on the bright side', which can be easily seen as dismissive and unempathetic. Instead, we suggest the survivor's life although irrevocably changed, is not over, and that in the future good things are possible."*
> (Briere & Scott, 2006)

ACTION #27

I can take steps for increasing my *positive emotions* such as joy, contentment, love, gratitude and happiness. I have the ability to look into the future and discover what will make me happy. I can create a "bucket list" of pleasurable emotionally uplifting activities that I can enjoy and that I want to do more often. I can also make a list of "safe" and engaging activities that I have not yet experienced, but that I would like to do. I can schedule "fun" activities. Now, that I have thought about the things I would like to do, I can now set out a schedule, anticipate possible obstacles, and *just do it!* I can engage fully in an *upward emotional spiral* of pleasurable, happiness—enhancing activities. Positive emotions do not just come by themselves. I can do something about them; broaden and enjoy life to a fuller extent.

"Don't wait to get sick to figure out what makes me happy."

Useful Information

People who engage in such happiness-generating activities live longer, get sick less often, and cope with stress more effectively.

Let us take a moment to consider, "What makes you truly happy?" Take a moment and answer the following *Hinge Questions:*

- "What do I enjoy doing most?"

- "What do I value most?"

- "What is most important to me?"

- "Who are the people who make me most happy?"

- "What can I do to increase my level of happiness?"

- "What is it that makes life worth living?"

- "What matters most to me in my life?"

Stephen Joseph, Ph.D., has offered the following exercise as a way to help individuals determine what makes them happy.

> *"Imagine suddenly waking up on a desert island, knowing that you will have to live the rest of your life there. Take a few minutes to reflect on the people you would miss most. Then reflect on the places and the activities you would miss. List all of these people, places and activities. Now think about how much time you spend with the people on your list, visiting those places and doing those activities. Now choose one person, one place, and one activity and make a commitment to yourself and write out a contract to yourself promising to do this. Such an imaginary exercise can help individuals formulate the reasons to be happy. Once such reasons are found, then happiness will ensue."*
>
> (Joseph, 2011)

Now, consider some of the answers offered by others like yourself.

> *The largest determinant of* happiness *is having a supportive network of close relationships. Happiness is a collective phenomenon and positive emotions spread through social networks. For example, recent research has found that the acquisition of money like winning a lottery does make people happier, but only if they spend it on other people, rather than on themselves.*

In addition, Sonja Lyubomirsky has indicated that the following activities have been found to contribute to happiness:

- Practice acts of kindness, caring, compassion to others and to oneself. No act of kindness, no matter how small is ever wasted.

- Invest your time and energy in family and friends. Seek opportunities to connect.

- Contribute to the welfare of others. Make a positive difference in the world. Act like a good house guest who wants to leave this place in better shape than he/she found it.

- Develop a life purpose, especially one that is not just about you.

- Count your blessings, rather than your burdens.

- Be optimistic.

- Appreciate life's joys. Pursue the small pleasures of life.

- See the "spark of decency" in others.

- Never lose sight of the strengths and virtues that reside within you.

- Thank a mentor. Express appreciation.

- Make a gift of your experiences (lessons learned) with others.

- Develop and practice strategies of coping with stress.

- Identify and share your "strengths," "islands of competence" with others.

- Possess a sense of humor and be playful.

- Take care of your body.

Remember that the happiest people do not necessarily have the best of everything; they just make the best of everything they have. See the following Website for additional descriptions of happiness-engendering activities: Visit *www.authentic hapiness.com.*

Quotable Quotes

"Live with vision and purpose. Resilient people don't wait passively for the future to happen to them. They become the future by consciously creating it. The present is pregnant with the possible."

—Joan Borysenko

"There is a saying that yesterday is history, tomorrow is a mystery, and today is a gift. That is why it's called the 'present.'"

ACTION #28

I believe in perseverance; the passionate pursuit of long-term goals and "true grit." As noted by Angela Duckworth and her colleagues (2007), *grit* is a passion to undertake and complete a mission with an unswerving dedication and determination to achieve that mission whatever the obstacles. *Grit* is a sense of steadfastness, sustainability and pride. In order to determine your level of *grit*, how many of the following items characterize you? Can you give examples of each?

- "I concentrate my efforts on doing something about the situation."

- "I do what has to be done, one step at a time."

- "I try to come up with a strategy or game plan about what to do."

- "I try to get advice from someone about what to do."

- "I finish whatever I begin."

- "I have achieved a goal that took years of work."

- "I have overcome setbacks to conquer an important challenge."

- "Setbacks don't discourage me."

- "When I put my mind to something I can work strenuously to achieve it."

- "I can maintain effort and interest over a long period of time (years), despite failure, adversities and plateaus in progress."

- "I can set long-term objectives and not swerve from them even in the absence of positive feedback."

- "I am eager to explore new things."

- "I believe that effort will improve my future."

- "I have zeal and the capacity for hard work."

- "I have a sustained commitment to my ambition."

- "I have confidence in my ability to make this transition to civilian life."

- "I show tenacity across life experiences."

"I can choose the 'hard right', over the 'easy wrong'."

Useful Information

Grit has proven to be an important predictor of who completes Special Forces Training and other Missions. Grit contributes to *resilience*.

Quotable Quotes

"I believe that facing a challenge is when learning truly occurs."

"I have learned how to swim against the tide."

"I believe that pain and suffering are triggers for personal growth."

"When I was down range, life was good for me, as well as hard. But it was full with little time to feel sorry for myself. I liked the routines and security. Now, I am in the business of creating my own routines, schedule and security."

"Life needs to have a forward lean toward engagement, purpose and perseverance."

"I can show "grit" which is the passion to pursue long-term goals and the ability to stick to it in order to fulfill my personal mission. I can map out my needs and resources. I can unleash my abilities and make greater use of my resources. I can stay the course and be determined."

Consider the following accounts for an example of true grit:

"The RPG (Rocket Propelled Grenade) ambush in Fallujah, Iraq destroyed his upper palate, and his left eye. It pulverized his left arm and right leg. It took sixty operations and six years to recover. One thing kept him going. He wanted to return to his men. He is now in command of 150 infantrymen, armor soldiers during their one year tour in Afghanistan. His men accept him, even though he can't see out of his left eye, and he eats with prosthesis. He is the most seriously injured active-duty soldier. His name is Army Captain D.J. Skelton." (Esquire Magazine, Dec. 2011)

"The RPG blast of her Humvee in Iraq collapsed her right lung and led to the amputation of her right arm. She reports that deep-down, 'I have not changed. I don't walk around all day looking at a mirror. I'm myself.' But there are moments that catch her by surprise. 'Oh my gosh, I only have one arm. I get anxious. It is never going to be easy.' In spite of her injuries and losses, she went on to demonstrate courage, a warrior spirit, thriving in the recovery from war. She evidenced what Plato called 'thumos'—a kind of 'fire in the belly' that is essential to the reintegration process. 'There is also anxiety, frustration, fatigue, phantom pain, restricted mobility, self-pity, embarrassment, shame and a wish to retreat. There is mourning for the past and what she once could do. And there is also happiness.' Through grit and a can-do attitude she is now the founder and CEO of a 100 per-

son defense contracting firm which she started after leaving Walter Reed Hospital. She drives, uses a BlackBerry, plays tennis left-handed, and does yoga. Her name is Dawn Halfaker. You can read her account and others like her in Nancy Sherman's The untold war. You can also see an interview with Dawn in a wonderful HBO movie, Alive Day Memories." (Sherman, 2010)

Quanitta Underwood was ten years old and her sister was twelve years old when they were regularly sexually abused by their father. The psychiatric wounds and suicidal attempts are told in a New York Times story (February 12, 2012) and on Quanitta's website *www.livingoutthedream.org*. It is a story of resilience, as Quanitta (known as Queen), is the five-time U.S. female boxing champion and is rated fourth in the world, and is also competing in the Olympics.

"Quanitta, a girl who felt like a nobody, but always imagined there was a somebody within. That's why she called her website 'Living Out The Dream'…I am a survivor of child abuse, and I became strong and independent… That dream carried me through a lot of days." (Barry Bearak, 2012)

ACTION #29

I use and enjoy positive humor. I can laugh at myself and keep things in perspective. I can laugh hard with someone else, since shared laughter is a way to make and keep friends. I can tell my story with a "twist" at the end. As the author Mark Twain observed: "I have had many catastrophes in my life, some of which actually happened."

Useful Information

Resilient individuals tend to laugh a lot which lubricates their brain, as well as their relationships. Laughter triggers "feel good" chemicals in the brain. Humor lessens stress levels, enhances mood, supports immune function and healing, and strengthens coping abilities.

Find something to laugh about each day. Ask your partner, "What happened today that made you laugh?" Individuals with a sense of humor are more fun to be with and this leads to good times together, better relationships and more *resilience*. (See the website *www.ajokeaday.com* as a way to tend your mind and refresh your spirit.)

Quotable Quotes

"When I got to Iraq my commanding officer gave each of us a marble to carry with us. He told us, 'Iraq is dangerous. Don't lose your marbles.' I still have that marble with me now that I am home. It is a reminder." (See www.survivalortist.com "A Marble in the Sand")

"When POWs were asked what the secret of their endurance was, they often mentioned joking, sharing funny observations and laughing as effective coping methods—specifically, joking about the enemy. Such jokes and laughter helped to create and maintain a sense of solidarity and companionship."

ACTION #30

I can express *gratitude* which is an emotion and *be grateful*. I convey my appreciation to those who have helped me. (Say "Thank you" and "Please"). Gratitude also refers to noticing and appreciating the positive aspects of life and feeling awe when encountering beauty in the world.

Gratitude is to the past what hope is to the future and it can serve as a sort of "pump primer" for hope. Gratitude is the soil from which positive emotions like joy flourish. Appreciation is like an investment in your own strengths. As Cicero observed, "Gratitude is not only the greatest of all the virtues, but the parent of all other virtues."

Useful Information

People who are grateful tend to be less depressed, angry, hostile and less emotionally vulnerable. They experience positive emotions like happiness more frequently, have better social relationships and have better conflict resolution skills. Gratitude serves to find, remind and bind people to caring individuals in their lives. Grateful individuals are more willing to forgive others and themselves. They derive health benefits and they even sleep better than individuals who are infrequently grateful.

Gratitude confers resilience and builds interpersonal bonds and "social currency" that can be cashed in or traded in when needed.

How To: Steps to Improve My Level of Gratitude and Make Gratitude a Daily Habit

1. Keep a "Gratitude Diary," a log or running account on a nightly basis of one to three things for which I am grateful or that went well during the day, or helpful and grateful caring acts I performed that day. They may be small things or big things. (See *www.gratitudelog.com* for an example of such a Gratitude Diary procedure).

2. Reflect daily on something for which I am grateful (grateful contemplation) and what this experience meant to me.

3. Create a list of my "top three peak experiences" and now visualize them in my mind. How does this make me feel?

4. Behavioral expressions of gratitude. Express gratitude to someone I have never properly thanked. Write a letter to a benefactor, mentor or helper thanking him/her for assistance; visit the person and read the letter.

5. Increase kind acts. Be helpful to others, altruistic. Spice up kindness. Put my gratitude "in the bank of social currency" that I can call upon later.

6. Use my "signature strengths" and "islands of competence" in new ways to help others.

7. Give examples for the following:

   a. "I have so much in life to be thankful for."

   b. "I am really thankful for friends and family."

   c. "I reflect on how fortunate I am to have basic things in life like food, clothing and shelter."

   d. "When I see natural beauty, I feel like a child who is awestruck."

   e. "I stop and enjoy my life as it is. I can stop and smell the roses."

   f. "I realize life is short. Thinking about dying reminds me to live every day to the fullest."

   g. "When I see someone less fortunate than myself I realize how lucky I am."

   h. "I am grateful for that which I have and do not long for that which I do not have."

   i. "Being content is a gift I give myself."

Remember I can move forward by giving back and moving from "me" to "we." Consider the following example offered by an NCO:

"I talked to my eight-year-old son last night. He told me about an award he won at school, and usually, I'd just say something like 'that's nice'. But I used the skill on how to show gratitude by asking a bunch of questions about it. 'Who was there when he got the award? How did he feel receiving it? Where's he going to hang the award? And about halfway through the conversation he interrupted me and said, 'Dad is this really you?' I know what he meant by that. This was the longest we ever talked, and I think we were both surprised by it."

How To: Regulate Negative Emotions

Emotional regulation is the process by which individuals influence which emotions they have, when they have them, and how they experience and express them.

This section will provide specific ways you can ensure that your emotions/feelings do not get in the way of your achieving your personal goals. These are practical steps you can take preemptively before an emotion is fully felt and constructive steps you can take after an emotion is experienced.

There are different ways to handle emotions. Sometimes individuals conceal their emotions (suppress, clam up, use distractions and avoidant strategies); other times individuals work to self-regulate their emotions (control, reframe and share their feelings with supportive others); and other times individuals learn to tolerate their emotions (be open to experience their feelings, ride out their emotions, accept their feelings).

There is no right way to handle emotions. It depends on what the situation demands and what are the individual's personal goals. Emotionally-fit and resilient individuals are flexible in choosing what strategy they use as incorporated in a form of psychotherapy known as Dialectical Behavior Therapy as described by Koerner and Linehan (2011).

ACTION #31

I need to understand that emotionally aroused individuals may learn to use "opposite actions." They behave in a manner that results in new ways of thinking and feeling.

- *"Instead of* avoiding situations, reminders, suppressing thoughts, I can talk to a supportive person."

- *"Instead of* withdrawing or drinking or taking drugs, I can engage in a pleasurable, healthy activity like exercise."

- *"Instead of* having harmful addictions, I can develop a positive addiction."

- *"Instead of* attacking someone because of my anger, I can take a time out and talk about it later when I cool down."

- *"Instead of* trying to control my emotions, I can learn to *accept* them and let them just run their course."

- *"Instead of* reacting and avoiding my distressing thoughts and feelings, I can acknowledge, label, tolerate and embrace them.

- *"Instead of* letting these trauma events keep control of my feelings, behaviors and decisions, I will gain the upper hand and start to control how I think.

- *"Instead of* inhibiting my emotions, I can have an emotional release and have a good cry or get it off my chest."

- *"Instead of* stuffing my feelings and trying to keep them out of sight, I can understand them better, name them, and share them with trusted others."

- *"Instead of* becoming self-absorbed with the past or the future, I can focus my attention on moment-to-moment experiences that are constantly occurring in the present."

- *"Instead of* dwelling on the past, I can come to terms with my history, and perhaps even grow beyond it."

- *"Instead of* putting myself and others down, I can *free myself* from the judgmental aspects of my story-telling."

- *"Instead of* being defensive, I can be more open and accepting of experiences."

- *"Instead of* getting uptight, I can contain my emotions in order to get the job done, remaining calm and focused."

- *"Instead of* focusing on over learned childhood-era criticism and accompanying self-talk, I can explicitly disagree with such thoughts and view them as "old tapes," rather than as accurate perceptions."

- *"Instead of* feeling that I do not deserve happiness and a good quality of life, I can engage life, have fun and enjoy the moment."

- *"Instead of* choosing denial and avoidance, blocking awareness ('letting sleeping dogs lie'), I can choose a braver choice and confront my memories and accompanying distress and *integrate* them into the fabric of my life story."

"I can learn to change my emotions by acting opposite to my current emotions. I can learn that acting like I feel good can make it so."

Engaging in opposite actions means changing what I do and how I do it. It involves changing how I think, my body posture, facial expressions, what I say and how I say it.

ACTION #32

I give myself permission to be sad, cry, grieve, and become angry without becoming aggressive. These are *all* normal healthy emotions. Think of my emotions as "commodities" or "things" that I do something with. The question is *what does one do with his/her emotions*? Do I "stuff them"? Suppress them? Keep them to myself? Act out? Feel sorry for myself? And if I do these things with my emotions, then I can ask myself:

"What is the impact on me and on others?"
"What is the toll or price that I and others pay?"
"Is this the way I want things to be?"
"What can I do differently?"

Instead of burying or avoiding emotions, I can allow or embrace my feelings, without becoming consumed or knocked off balance by them. There are resources to help me cope more effectively with distressing emotions like depression and anxiety. Visit the website *www.beatingtheblues.co.uk* for a self-help computer-based cognitive-behavioral treatment.

Useful Information

Keep in mind that I can have an emotion without having to act upon it. Negative and positive emotions can co-occur, and exist side-by-side. Individuals may hold beliefs that inhibit their sharing their feelings. Do you hold any of the following attitudes, and if so, what is the impact on you and on others?

1. I think you should always keep your feelings under control.

2. I think you are right not to burden other people with your problems.

3. I think getting emotional is a sign of weakness.

4. I think other people do not understand my feelings.

Quotable Quotes

"If I bottle up my toxic emotions, I am more likely to cause unintended harm to others and to myself."

"Instead of keeping my emotions under wraps, I can share them with someone I trust and who is supportive."

"Instead of drinking my bad feelings away and letting my bitterness eat me alive, I can ask for help and not let the war define me."

"I can now accept my feelings without ignoring them or feeling guilty or ashamed."

"I can handle my emotions constructively and identify and express them when needed."

"I can put powerful emotions 'on hold' until the danger has passed."

"I can dose myself and deal with my emotions at my own pace, in my own time, and in my own way."

"I can learn to accept the fact that some circumstances cannot be changed."

"I tried really hard to make sense out of it, and at one point I realized that I could not have it all. I have realized how small I am; I'm actually much weaker than I thought. And in a way I appreciate having the chance that made me realize my limits; otherwise, I would be more arrogant and take a haughty attitude toward everything. I have to admit that before I thought no matter what happened I would be able to cope with it. Apparently, I was ignorant. I'm not that special. There are some things that I cannot do anything about. I just have to accept that."

ACTION #33

I learn how to face my fears and operate outside of my "comfort zone." I can have courage and recognize that fear is normal and that it can act as a guide. I can visualize what I want to have happen, rather than worrying about what I fear. I can *avoid avoidance.* Avoidance only makes my fears worse (See Action #72 and *www.anxieties.com* for suggestions on ways to handle anxieties).

I need to check out the "facts." Is the threat a realistic fear or am I over blowing the situation? What has to happen for this situation to be less emotional? What can I do to ensure safety and feel more in control?

Think of a fear you have overcome in the past. How did you handle this? Individuals handle their fears by having the courage to do (confront) the very things they feared. Through repeated exposure, what you feared loses its potency to evoke such fearful emotions and accompanying avoidant behaviors. How can you apply such "courage" to any remaining fears you may have?

Useful Information

Treatments for individuals with Post Traumatic Stress Disorder focus on reducing trauma-related anxiety by encouraging the client to confront situations, activities, thoughts, memories and feelings that are feared and avoided, but that are not inherently dangerous. Avoidance behaviors are the major factor that contribute to chronic PTSD and interfere with the resolution of emotions.

Quotable Quotes

"I have learned to reduce my fears by reducing avoidance and confronting previously avoided and feared situations."

"I have learned to break the habit of avoiding."

"For a long time, I feared my memories of what I experienced. Such avoidance only made things worse."

"I had a phobic avoidance of all trauma-related events and reminders."

"It is like the classic example of when an animal is fed something at a given location in his cage and it makes him sick and nauseated. No matter how many times one feeds the animal good food at that location, the animal will resist and will not voluntarily go there to collect available food. Like that avoidant animal, I have to learn to approach, rather than avoid. This is where courage comes into play."

ACTION #34

I engage in constructive grieving, honoring and memorializing those who have died. I can recall "cherished memories" of those who have been lost. Unrecognized and unresolved grief can take a toll. It is critical to honor those who died. Remember, that which is mentionable is manageable. Efforts to ignore grief will actually make it worse (See the website *www.griefnet.org*).

Grief is a form of "emotional energy." Do not hesitate to use it—write, paint, pray, garden, listen to music, cry, memorialize, commemorate. Moving forward is *not* a selfish act. Do it for yourself and others. For those who try to comfort the grief-stricken, it is worth keeping in mind the observations of Gail Sheehy who wrote poignantly about the surviving family members of the victims of the 9/11 terrorist attack (Sheehy, 2003). She observed:

> *"People in deep grief want to feel that you heard their pain. If you try to 'fix it', you may rob them of that passage. They often want someone that they can trust, cry with, and confess to, someone who is nonjudgmental. Remember it is a privilege to be part of the healing process."*
>
> —Gail Sheehy

> *"Bereavement is not a disease. Bereavement is not packaged so that it is all fixed or resolved by a certain period of time. Thoughts, memories, and sadness may return over many years, as may a sense of unfinished business with the deceased. Nevertheless, functioning and interpersonal relations continue as does adapting to getting on with life without the deceased."*
>
> —Beverly Raphael and Sally Wooding

Useful Information

Loss is universal, and grief will be some of the hardest work you will ever do. Even though it is hard, it is important that you do it. Time alone does not heal all wounds, but it is what you *do* with that time that matters. Grieving is an active process that continues and changes over time. Healing from loss does not mean that you forget. Healing means that you carry your memories from a place of pain to a place of love and honor in your life.

Some trauma survivors have found it helpful to resolve their "unresolved emotional business" by using a guided mourning intervention such as an "empty chair exercise." Using imagination, the bereaved individual can have a conversation with the deceased person telling him/her what the loss meant to them, what has changed in them and in their behavior since the loss, using the present tense. They then consider and describe how the deceased person would respond to them after hearing what has just been said. What would the deceased person want for the grieving loved one? What forgiveness-related and resilience-building comments would the deceased person offer? What would he/she want for their friend or loved one, if the situation were reversed?

Another memorial strategy that some folks have found helpful is to write a letter addressed to the deceased person indicating how he or she is being remembered and what lingers from the relationship and how this is being used each and every day. There are many other cultural, ethnic and religious ways particular groups memorialize and honor those who have died. Find a way that is most comfortable and meaningful for you.

Social sharing and public expressions of grief and emotions connected with the tragedy can strengthen a sense of solidarity, trust and hope. Such shared activities mobilize collective memories and foster community networks. For example, after the terrorist bombing in Madrid, Spain the people's participation in public demonstrations and community commemorative services helped individuals develop a sense of solidarity with others. "People came here to be united, to share their pain, to stay together and to have a feeling of belonging." Participation in memorial ceremonies, active citizen engagement in political activities and demonstrations acts to bolster *resilience*.

Quotable Quotes

"I learned several ways to bundle my grief. Express my feelings not swallow them and be patient. The growing process is not quiet. I had to remind myself to take care of my physical needs of eating right and getting enough sleep. Joining a support group also helped. Just being active helped."

"I learned I could live fully again, accompanied by my husband (deceased person) who is alive in my memory."

"I ask myself what would he like me to do if I was no longer grieving?"

"Dust to dust, ashes to ashes, you will always be with us." (You can bury in the ground or in the sea a memento of your deceased loved one.)

"The calls keep coming. After 9/11, they never found my son's body, but I keep getting calls whenever they find a body part. We filled his empty casket with reminders of the things he loved and buried them. I am collecting all of his body parts and I will have them buried with me."

—A bereaved mother of a firefighter

"Somehow, the memories of all my friends who died of AIDS were less and less about the hard times and the illness and more and more about the happy times. I came to see him (my partner who died of AIDS) more as my angel looking over me and helping me."

—An AIDS Survivor

"As I stood at his gravesite, I remembered that his obituary said, 'He was an ordinary man who, by his words and actions, did extraordinary things.' I had the thought that it was my fervent hope that the rest of my days are a fitting tribute to the life he never will have the chance to live himself."

—Major Andrew J. Dekever, "Dealing with Dead"
(Notre Dame Magazine, Autumn, 2011)

"Visiting the gravesite of those who died helped me remember to live a life worthy of their sacrifice, whose lives intersected mine during the Afghan War. I feel a sense of obligation to live my life on their behalf which gives me an added sense of purpose that has helped me make peace with my personal ordeal."

"The death of my friends in combat has made it hard for me to get on with my life. But I think what my buddies who died would want me to do. So I keep on going. I remember one buddy who I was close with would always tell me not to sweat the small stuff and appreciate the little things in life. I remember what he said. I guess that the best way to get back at those who hurt you is to live life well."

—Anonymous Marine who was deployed to Afghanistan

"I am a living tribute to all of my war buddies who died. They can't be forgotten. In their memories, I can come to terms with my experiences. Honoring my deceased comrades mitigates any feelings of guilt that I have."

"I thought about surrendering to my grief. But I had a plan. I focused on controlling my symptoms and on the life I have now. What it means and how much of a difference I had made in my husband's life. That sustains me."

"At my grandmother's funeral people visited or tried to comfort us. There are great people out there and I actually want to do something for the community."

Hinge Questions to consider if your grief is an ongoing problem (six months since the death of a loved one):

- Has anything like this ever happened to you before, where a loved one died?

- How did you handle that loss?

- What form does your grief take now?

- Does your grief interfere with your day to day activities? In what ways? Please be specific.

- When during the day do you find your grief is at its highest and it's lowest? Can you rate your grief intensity on a scale of 1 to 10? When is it worse (10); when does it improve (1)?

- If you were feeling much better and your grief was not so distressing and preoccupying, what do you think you would like to be doing differently?

- What would you need to be doing in order to know that you were moving forward?

- What could help you achieve this goal?

- What could stand in the way of your achieving your goal?

- How can you deal with the emotional side of the loss (feelings of sadness, guilt, shame, anxiety, anger), at the same time you are rebuilding your life?

- Is there anyone who can help you work on these goals?

- How can you tell you are making progress?

ACTION #35

I process my memories of bad experiences that I have had. Sharing my story permits me to gain conscious control over it. "I can control my story. I can let the past be the past. My story does *not* control me, I can choose which CD I play in my head. I can choose whether I am a 'victim', or a 'survivor', or even a 'thriver'." Keep in mind:

> *"Whoever survives a test*
> *Whatever it may be*
> *Must tell the story*
> *That is one's duty"*
> —Elie Wiesel

The Ancient Greek and Roman concept of the "Hero" is the story of an ordinary person who experiences an extraordinary event, survives, and returns to the everyday world to express an important truth about life.

Quotable Quotes

"I learned that thinking about the trauma is not the same as being in the trauma."

"I can live a valued life with my history, rather than living a life driven by my history."

"I can make room for different memories."

"Recovery from trauma is more a journey than a destination."

"I learned to leave the bad stuff I experienced in the background and get on with my life the best I can. It is always there, but I continue nonetheless."

"I no longer confuse the past with the present."

"Experience is not what happens to you; it's what you do with what happens to you"—Aldous Huxley.

ACTION #36

I can *tolerate distress* and handle and overcome my emotional pain that comes with feeling disconnected. I need to recognize how things have changed at home and on my job. I can now talk to someone about these feelings and begin to work out a "game plan" on what to do.

Quotable Quotes

"Coming from combat to home is not an easy task. It's hard to explain how I feel to anyone...I have changed a lot—some for the better, some for the worse. Before Iraq I didn't have any plans or goals. Now I do. I might not be as happy as I used to be, but I am getting there. Some days it's hard."

> —Anonymous U.S. soldier after returning from a 15 month deployment in Iraq

"I have developed a willingness to live with physical and emotional pain, while engaging in important daily activities. I have learned to control what I can and accept what I cannot control."

> —A wounded amputee service member

Useful Information

Instead of keeping my emotional pain to myself and stuffing feelings, I can reach out to others. For example, I can call the "Veterans Lifeline" (1-800-273-8255 or 1-

800-273-TALK). If you need immediate help, call 911. (See Action #81 for additional resources, websites and agencies).

ACTION #37

I use a "writing cure" of journaling; keep a running diary, blogging, social networking websites or testimony writing of what happened. I can write out the story of what I experienced, including any emotional "hot spots," "stuck points," and share these accounts with people I trust. Trauma resolved is a great gift that I can share with others. I can use the healing value of emotional expression. When people keep the trauma a secret then it can become toxic to one's health and social relationships. Expressive writing can enhance adjustment and bolster resilience.

Useful Information

Sharing one's account in the form of journaling or story-telling is the mind's attempt to heal itself. Unresolved memories of trauma have to be talked about and re-experienced so they can be processed. Avoidance just keeps symptoms alive. Journaling permits you to relive the past while viewing it from the perspective of the present and helps you perform a "guided reconsideration." Journaling permits you to become both a narrator and spectator of your life experiences. Like someone on the outside looking in, you can develop a perspective that you might not have had before.

Research by Jamie Pennebaker and his colleagues have found that when individuals engage in expressive writing about stressful and traumatic events it has a number of positive outcomes including medical consequences of reducing visits to doctors by breast cancer patients and migraine and respiratory sufferers, reduced absenteeism from work, improved grade point averages for students, and improved relationships and reduced PTSD and overall lowered levels of psychological distress in trauma victims. The writing out of a trauma narrative alone is not sufficient to improve psychological and physical health, but that it is also essential to integrate thoughts and feelings about the traumatic events into a consistent and meaningful account.

Expressive writing has been utilized with a variety of psychological problems (e.g. anxiety, depression) and stress resulting from medical diagnoses, job loss, and loss of a significant other (through death, relationship break up).

When individuals included in their expressive writing words that reflect insight, change and a search for meaning and causality, it propelled personal growth. Such words as "know, consider, understand, purpose" and "because, cause, effect" provide a basis for behavioral change. See Action #62 and #65 for a list of RE- and Action verbs that you can include in your healing journal writing.

Developing a "coherent narrative" is an essential element of post-traumatic growth. Writing encourages you to make sense of your experiences and integrate what happened into your autobiographical memory. You can also use the expressive writing technique to journal about your reintegration experiences, not just your deployment experiences.

For practical advice on writing see: homepage.psy.utexas.edu/homepage/Faculty/Pennebaker/Home2000/Writingandhealth.html

Pennebaker suggests that you write for at least fifteen minutes a day for four consecutive days. You can also keep a written diary of what is going well.

Quotable Quotes

"Give sorrow words: the grief that does not speak; whispers the o're-fraught heart and bids it break."

—Shakespeare's MacBeth

"What cannot be talked about can also not be put to rest; and if it is not, the wounds continue to fester from generation to generation."

—Bruno Bettleheim

"I write in order to discover what I am thinking."

—Joan Didion

"It takes a lot of courage to write down the traumatic experiences that you have had. It makes it more real."

"As the words and emotions came pouring out, I realized this was my form of therapy."

"When I started keeping this diary, at first I thought it would not prove helpful. What amazed me was that after a week I was able to fill up a couple of pages. When I read these items each night I realized I was on the road to recovery."

"Give yourself permission to express your feelings in writing or talk them out with someone who can relate to what you feel. This is what I found was most helpful."

Finally, it is worth noting that such expressive writing has been found to be helpful at both the individual and communal levels. For example, as part of the healing process in postwar Kosovo (which was previously part of Yugoslavia) and where a civil war occurred, they have created the Archives of Memory project, in which they collected stories of Kosovars following the war. Such shared, documented "story-telling" contributed to posttraumatic growth and *resilience*.

At the individual level, traumatized and victimized clients have used journaling in a treatment procedure called Cognitive Processing Therapy (CPT) (*see www.cpt. musc.edu*).

How To: Journal and Engage in Guided Reconsideration

Journaling can help individuals understand the meaning of the traumatic event, with an emphasis on identifying how the events changed an individual's beliefs about self, other people, the world and the future. Journaling can help individuals identify and challenge "stuck points" which are the problematic beliefs and conclusions regarding the nature and meaning of the traumatic experiences. Journaling helps individuals to organize their memories of the trauma, develop a stronger sense of self-control and experience less distress in response to internal and external reminders.

1. To begin with try and write out a page or two of what traumatic encounter(s) you experienced. Include as much detail about it as you can remember. Be specific as possible and include your deepest feelings about these events. The account should be written in the present tense. (Some have found that writing about negative events in the third person perspective is most helpful).

2. You may wish to begin with "broad strokes" and then fill in the picture with specific details. For instance, what happened, what feelings you had, what thoughts you had when it happened, what anyone else said or did, and what you did right afterward?

3. You do not have to do this all at once. It may take several attempts to get it all down.

4. After you are all done writing, read your account to yourself at least once before sharing it with a supportive other like a counsellor or chaplain. You can repeatedly reread your narrative.

5. If it is too upsetting to read all at once, try reading as much as you can, and then read the rest when you are able.

6. Revisit your account and add what you did to survive and consider what lingers from this experience. What conclusions do you draw about yourself, about other people and about the future, as a result of this experience?

7. The mere act of writing about upsetting events, especially if done on multiple occasions can reduce psychological distress over time.

8. How do you now feel about what you have experienced since sharing this with yourself and supportive others?

9. You can also journal about growth-related benefits that followed from the traumatic event.

10. You can write about these events for fifteen to thirty minutes on three to five consecutive days.

Other Ways to Use Journaling and Letter Writing

1. Write a supportive and encouraging letter to an imaginary friend who has experienced the loss of a loved one and who is facing difficulties. In the letter address the following questions:

   a. Is it possible that your friend has learned something through the death of his/her loved one or through what happened after the loss?

   b. Has he/she found out something about life which he/she would otherwise not have seen at all?

   c. Is this knowledge useful in other areas of his/her life?

   d. Has this experience changed his/her in a positive sense?

   e. Can you use any of the answers you included in your letter on yourself?

2. You can write a "rainy day" letter to yourself indicating what changes you have made, "signs of resilience and recovery." You can describe yourself sympathetically in the third person. This letter can be read when you feel the need.

3. Write a letter from the future, namely, "as if" several years have passed including in your letter positive events that you would like to have happen, have indeed happened.

4. Torture victims have written "testimonials" of atrocities they have experienced and shared in groups their accounts with other survivors. They have included in their testimonials what acts of justice they wish to pursue.

5. Holocaust survivors have made video testimonials conveying their memories of events in order to leave a legacy. Healing through sharing. Consider the many war-torn accounts of combat that document the impact of trauma.

Journaling makes the thoughts and feelings about events more organized and coherent. Writing forces one's thoughts to become more structured, less fragmented, fosters insight and reframing, acceptance and closure, perspective taking and problem-solving, nurturing hope.

ACTION #38

I use creative and expressive techniques to process my feelings like one on one conversations with my Battle Buddies when I am fishing/hunting, working on my car, writing in my personal diary, playing my guitar, going dancing, engaging in various "healing" rituals.

Useful Information

The Greeks used theater as a means to help individuals address the feelings accompanying traumas such as combat. This type of "community catharsis experience" is now being employed by the military in their Theatre of War Program (*www.theatre-of-war.com*), so service members and their family members can better understand the impact of military experiences and destigmatize help-seeking. As has been observed, "The more things change, the more they remain the same."

ACTION #39

I enjoy the benefits of self-disclosing to a trusted friend, family member, battle buddy, fellow soldier who is understanding, receptive and supportive.

Useful Information

As noted, and worth repeating, disclosure and sharing with others leads to less avoidance and fewer stress-related consuming thoughts. A trusted friend may offer new ways of understanding and a different view of things. He or she may ask about one's "strengths" and survival skills.

Quotable Quotes

"There is no greater agony than bearing an untold story inside of you."
　　　　　　　　　　　　　　　　　　　　—Maya Angelou

"What people need is a companion alongside them in their journey to rebuild their lives."

"When something like this happens things can never be the same again. They just can't. Life is different. When I try to go back, that is when I get stuck. I can't escape things happening in life. What I have to do is confront my experiences and learn from them. But, I can't do this alone."

ACTION #40

I "RE-story" my life experiences and share my account of resilience ("the rest of the story"), as a legacy work with my family members, friends and battle buddies.

Useful Information

Memory can "skip" when going through traumatic memories. It remembers some things very vividly and forgets other things which are important for resilience. Under extreme stress, the normal memory processes do not work as usual; because we are so busy trying to survive. The body gets so busy making muscles work, and takes "off-line" those things that are not important like memory. It is like a CD or DVD player skipping when it is bumped. If one has experienced stressful events, it is important to regain an image of oneself as a "survivor" and to understand that he/she has control over how that image (or the "skips" in memory) is filled back in and how it is integrated, incorporated into one's "life story." A person has the ability to get unstuck from the "hot spots" or "stuck points" and increase his/her ability to be *resilient*.

Quotable Quotes

"By telling and retelling my story I can create opportunities for new meanings and new stories to emerge."

"I can now RE-construct my history in the present and create a new future."

"I recognize that I am not in total control of my life, but I can choose how I perceive my experiences."

"I am not at the mercy of my emotions. I can create a new self-map."

ACTION #41

I manage my strong emotions (anxiety, depression, anger, guilt, shame, moral injuries). I can rein in the emotional part of my brain, and control my emotions *before* they have a negative impact on me and on others around me. Negative emotions are signals that something is wrong and that there is a difference between the way a thing is and how I want it to be. Emotions are a trigger to activate my action plans, like asking for help or using my *mindfulness* and *tactical breathing*, or some other coping skills.

How To: Steps to My Emotional Fitness: Things I Can Do to Help Feel More In Control

- Tune into my feelings, monitor and "spot check" how I am feeling. I have the ability to control my attention and choose what "emotional channel" I will select. I can learn my bodily clues of distress ("My telltale signs of stress are..."). Spot early warning signs.

- Name or label my feelings. ("Do I feel angry, afraid, sad, hurt, confused, frustrated, guilty, ashamed, calm, grateful?") Naming the emotion helps me regulate how I feel and control my brain. If I can *name it*, I can *tame it.*

- Locate the feelings in my body and use my coping skills to manage my emotions. I can learn to "decondition" my intense emotions and get grounded. When I notice that my mind is "spacing out" and I am taking on that "thousand mile stare," I can use my emergency procedure of "getting grounded" by bringing myself back to the present. I can refocus my attention to the immediate environment by describing in detail the external environment, naming the location of where I am, colors, sensations, and remind myself that I am "here and now" and in a "safe situation," instead of time-sliding back to the past. I can reorient and use my breathing retraining exercises. I can regulate down and deescalate my intense emotions and reduce the hold of my memories. Remind myself that the past is just a memory, not really happening right now.

  Another way to control my emotions and negative self-talk and refocus on the present is to use some form of self-stimulation. For example, get some ice cubes and hold them in your hands. This is a way to stop your mind from wandering and reduce your "mental chatter." It stops the Amygdala (part of your brain) from hijacking your emotions. If you cannot access ice cubes, you can take the stem of your watch and press it hard into your skin, not so hard to do damage, but just a reminder of the here and now. Another way to get grounded is to take a rubber band and place it around your wrist. Snap it when you notice you are reengaging in your negative self-talk habits. In this way you can learn to refocus your attention.

- Increase my "trigger awareness," namely the situational cues, my warning signs, red flags, both external cues (what people say or do, or what they fail to say or do), as well as internal cues (my feelings, thoughts, flashbacks, memories and cravings). I can ask myself, "What was happening before the feeling began?" I can avoid being blind-sided by reminders. I can learn to detect my "trip wires," "mental icebergs," or deeply held beliefs that lead to emotional over-reactions, "hot button issues" that "light my fuse." I can ask myself the following *Hinge Questions:*

  - "Are my present feelings and thoughts too intense and over-reactive based on the current situation of what just happened?"

  - "Do my initial thoughts and feelings carry with them memories of past trauma?"

  - "Are these 'old tapes' playing out or 'old anger' coming out?"

  - "Is this situation where I usually get triggered?"

- • "Can I engage in 'clever guessing' by hypothesizing or figuring out what is triggering my emotional state?"

- • "What happened right before I got upset/angry/scared?"

- • "Can I identify and prepare for such possible triggers?"

- Tolerate and accept my negative feelings and unwanted thoughts. Stay centered and follow the rise and fall of my emotions ("Like riding a wave"). Acceptance means letting myself experience my emotions without ignoring them or feeling guilty or ashamed, nor trying to change or challenge them.

- *Be actively mindful.* What is mindfulness training? What are the benefits of being mindful? How can I engage in mindfulness?

  "Mindfulness is paying attention on purpose, in the present moment, non-judgmentally."
  —Jon Kabat-Zinn

Mindfulness is a learnable set of skills, involving ongoing, moment-by-moment focused awareness and openness to the here and now without judgment and with acceptance. Mindfulness training involves the deliberate intention to pay attention to momentary experiences and a clear focus on all aspects of moment-to-moment experiences. Mindfulness is an increased awareness to everything that is going on around you, being in the present time and place without interference from the past or the future. Being mindful means identifying one's thoughts and feelings without getting stuck in them. It requires an attitude of openness, acceptance, kindness, curiosity and patience in order to engender feelings of tranquility and equanimity. A dispassionate, nonjudgmental, nonevaluative and sustained awareness can contribute to mindfulness. It is a polar opposite of avoidance. Mindfulness training helps individuals learn to realize that one's thoughts are only thoughts, and one's feelings are only feelings-not necessarily accurate information or reflection about the reality of the situation. Mindfulness is the ability to observe one's thoughts and feelings without getting stuck in them, nor growing them. By staying in the present with emotional pain, the mind develops the ability to process painful aspects of the past so these memories lose much of their emotional sting.

Mindfulness activities have been found to have mental and physical health benefits. Mindfulness contributes to enhanced cognitive flexibility, decreased rumination, improved concentration, mental clarity and emotional regulation (less anxiety and depression), increased distress tolerance and improved ability to relate to others. At the physical level mindfulness training has been found to increase immune functioning, lower somatic distress, and alter brain functioning such as amygdala activity that is involved in emotional regulation.

How To: Do Mindfulness

a. Learn to notice, observe, be aware of, and describe your private experiences (emotions, sensations, thoughts), as you are experiencing them in the moment, even if the experience is distressing. You can be nonjudgmental and concentrate on one thing at a time by letting go of distractions. You can become an observer of your emotions, instead of engaging in some type of "escape" or "avoidance" behaviors. You can live in the present with awareness and work on improving the moment. You can develop a friendly accepting interest in my present experiences.

b. Slowly scan your entire body, starting with your toes. Notice any sensations in your body without trying to change them.

c. Notice your body sensation of each in and out breath. Direct your continuous focused attention on your breathing- - *inhale* and *exhale*. This is a good starting point for learning how to raise awareness. Close your eyes and with curiosity and being non-judgmental allow whatever emerges in your awareness to be there, letting it come and go. Mentally label your experiences such as smelling, feeling, thinking, as you sit for a few moments.

d. "What is happening right now?" "What are you feeling right now?" "What is your experience right now?" "Can you stay with what is happening right now?" "Can you allow and accept this feeling and stay in touch with it without reacting to it?" "If not, what is happening in your experience that is reacting to this feeling?"

For examples of mindfulness activities visit the following websites *www.mindful.org* and *www.umassmed.edu/Content.aspx?id=41252* and works by Dr. Kabat-Zinn, including *Full Catastrophe Living* (1990) and *Wherever You Go, There You Are (1994).*

- Let my feelings go. Release my feelings. Let them subside naturally. Allow them to float away, resting on a wave. My thoughts are like a sailboat resting on its moorings. Have the ability to calm my mind and quiet my thinking. Pay attention to my breathing. Immerse myself in the pleasure of the moment. Develop the ability to move in and out of strong emotional states.

- Distance myself from my emotions by engaging in some other activity such as exercising, calming myself down, relaxing, using a pleasant memory or imagery, remembering a beautiful place or activity, change my self-talk or what I am telling myself, pray, seek soothing and comforting support and reassurance from others. Contemplative skills such as meditation and yoga and Chinese mindful movement practices such as tai chi and qui gong are associated with both physical and psychological benefits.

- Use my *relaxation skills*. Breathing is a key to relaxation. Use *tactical breathing* exercises and slow deep breathing to control arousal. I can also use muscle relaxation consisting of tensing and releasing various muscle groups, especially where I feel any tension. Control my attention and use positive imagery, meditation, yoga, or whatever works for me. Take a "time-out" and when I am calmed down, then call "time-in."

How To: Use Tactical Breathing

Tactical breathing involves learning how to use slow breathing, rather than hyperventilation or quick shallow breathing, or deep breathing. The body is physiologically more relaxed during the process of exhalation. Hyperventilation and shallow breathing can increase anxiety and associated physical symptoms such as muscle tension. The goal of Tactical Breathing Retraining is to learn to take normal breaths but to extend the process of exhaling to enhance relaxation.

Take a moment to conduct a "body scan." Ask yourself, "How do I feel in my body"? Use your body as a clue to find out how you might be feeling. Now begin by focusing your attention on your breathing. In order to more fully relax, your breathe out should be longer than your breathe in. For example, as you breathe out slowly count to ten then as you breathe in slowly count to six. Inhale slowly and then let the air out slowly. The air should flow over your lips, as if you were blowing on a spoon filled with hot soup and you did not want to spill it, just cool it down. Or imagine that you were exhaling slowly as if you were flickering a candle without blowing it out. Note the sensations of relaxation and calmness that develop. Try the following steps to further develop your ability to calm yourself down and stay relaxed.

1. Breathe in slowly for *six* counts
2. Hold for *two* counts
3. Breathe out for *ten* counts
4. Hold for *two* counts
5. Repeat

Feel free to alternate breathing in and breathing out to a count that best suits you. Just remember that the breath in count should be shorter than the breath out count.

In order to develop the skills of Relaxation and Tactical Breathing it takes practice like learning any other skill. First, find a comfortable chair and sit with your arms and legs uncrossed so you can learn how to practice diaphragmatic or calm breathing. The goal is to learn to breathe in through your nose and out through your mouth, with the air going all the way down to your lower belly. Tense or anxious breathing causes your upper chest to rise and fall, and the air only goes into your upper chest. Relax or calm breathing causes your lower stomach—

around your belly both to go up and down into your lower abdomen. Breathe in through your nose for a count of four and then hold the breath. As you breathe in your stomach will extend. Keep your chest still. Hold it. Now tighten your stomach muscles and notice your breath as you slowly breathe out through your mouth for a count of six.

Again breathe in through your nose …1, 2, 3, 4, with your stomach extending out. *Hold it*. Pay attention to your breath as you breathe out through your mouth: 1, 2, 3, 4, 5, 6 pulling your stomach muscles in. Remember to let the air go all the way down to your lower abdomen.

Stay in the moment. Begin to breathe more deeply into your abdomen, with the belly rising and falling with each breath. Imagine your breath coming in and out of your belly and into your chest like a wave. Now slow the breath down by counting to four with each inhalation and to six with each exhalation. As you exhale slowly, as if blowing on a spoon of hot soup without spilling it, say the word "relax" to yourself. Notice the sense of calmness and ease you have been able to bring forth. With practice, you will be able to learn to use this Relaxation Response whenever you feel stressed.

Tactical Breathing is what snipers use to calm their nerves and steady their hands. It can lower your heart rate by six to ten beats per minute that controls arousal and calms emotions. It can be used in any stressful situations, but it requires practice of at least 15 minutes a day. This practice is worthwhile because learning to use the Relaxation Response decreases muscle tension, reduces blood pressure, restores energy, turns off mental chatter, quiets down thinking, and fosters mindfulness. Find the best way for you to *relax*—meditation, mindfulness, imagery, yoga, prayer or tactical breathing.

• Use "safe place imagery." Think of an image that makes me feel safe and calm. It can be somewhere real or imagined, indoors or outdoors, with other people or on my own. Focus my mind on this image. Concentrate on my feelings of being calm. Think of a single word that captures this image like "breeze, beaches, mountain." Practice using this word to bring up the image and my feeling of being calm. By learning to find a safe image for myself, I will learn to calm my body down and take control of my reactions (feelings, thoughts and behaviors).

• Practice "containment." Hold my feelings in check in order to share and process them at a later time, in a safe place, with a trusted person.

• Compartmentalize—I can put worrisome thoughts aside for the moment since not doing something right now won't make a difference. I can come back to it later when I am better prepared to handle it. For example, write the specific thoughts and label the accompanying feelings on yellow posties. Then put the posties in an envelope labelled "Do Not Disturb." I can file these aside until later on so I can break the rumination cycle. I can take out these posties when I wish and can process them with someone else.

- I can persist in trying to achieve my goals even in the face of emotional distress. I can learn to tolerate psychological pain and accept it as part of my life, but it does not need to defeat me, define me, or control me. I can surprise myself and others by how I handle my feelings and behavior.

Our solutions to emotional and physical pain may keep us from recovering, by shutting us down just when we need to open up and process what has happened to us. In order to move out of pain, we have to sit with pain, even if we prefer to avoid this. The journey of a trauma survivor can require great courage and bravery to approach, rather than avoid, reaching out when isolation seems like a better idea.

- I can use my SOS Skills and improve my staying power in stressful situations. I can do things that help me feel better for at least thirty minutes (listen to music, exercise, call my best friend).

  S—Slow down and take a break, "turn down the volume," clear my mind, inhibit impulsive acts and be patient with myself and increase activities slowly

  O—Orient, pay attention to bodily senses and cues, both internal and external triggers, thoughts, and feelings

  S—Self-check, make rapid ratings of my current stress level and choose from my "coping kit"

- Anger is a strong predictor of the severity of PTSD, no matter what population one considers. The greater the level of anger and hostility, the slower the recovery process in crime victims, emergency relief workers, victims of torture, as well as in returning service members. A blaming style and an attitude of cynicism (view others as selfishly motivated), mistrusting (view others as being hurtful and intentionally provoking) and denigrating (view others in elevated terms as being stupid, ugly, deceitful, dishonest), will undermine the development of resilience. When such attitudes are paired with rumination (visualizing and recollecting "old hurts" and "old anger,)" plus the presence of substance abuse, a potential "powder keg" of emotions can be reactivated. In order to get from anger to aggression an important contributing factor is the attribution of intentionality, or the belief that the person did this "on purpose." These sets of thought are the lubricant that move individuals from being irritated and annoyed to the point of fury and rage.

Try a small experiment. Close your eyes for a moment and think of a situation that got you really angry. Now consider what would have to change in this situation, and in you, so you only felt annoyed, bothered and mildly angry? What do you have to say to yourself; what do you have to do and not do in order to reduce your anger thermometer? How would your self-talk have to change so you view the situation as a problem-to-be-solved, rather than as a personal threat, or as an instance of being wronged, disrespected and devalued?

When people are highly emotional, their thinking processes tend to be categorical ("seeing things as being either good or bad, black or white, stereotyping others"); personal ("seeing things as personal provocations and intentional"); action-oriented ("seeing oneself at risk and in need to fight, freeze or take flight"); and unreflective ("not consider the consequences of one's acts, nor consider alternative options").

Remember there is nothing wrong with the feeling of anger. It is what one does with the feelings of anger that is critical. Anger can be both helpful and unhelpful. Anger tells individuals that there is a difference between the way something is and the way they would like it to be. Anger tells individuals that there is a perceived "injustice" that needs correction. There would be no civil rights movement, women's liberation and other social change without anger. The key is what one does with one's anger.

- Pinpoint anger early and dampen arousal. Stay cool under fire. Identify and change the thoughts that fuel anger. Take a "time out" by saying:

    "This is important, but I need some time to calm down first."

    "I need a break. I need to chill before we talk this over."

Do not forget to call a "time in" afterward, using my communication skills.

Do not let my anger get control of me. I can change my relationship with my anger. I will not allow my temper to get the best of me. I will manage anger and not allow anger to manage me. For instance, I can:

- Watch out for red flags and warning signs.

- Learn to relax and turn down my arousal level.

- Take my Time Out and remember to call Time In.

- Rehearse what I want to say and do.

- View provocations as a problem-to-be-solved.

- Change my self-talk. Ask myself, "Is this really worth getting upset about?"

- Turn my anger into assertive responses.

- Avoid situations that make me angry.

- Let my anger and stubbornness go so I do not stew in my 'hostile juices.'

- Override my negative emotions, and not harbor grudges forever.

- Get help if I need it.

- Stay the course. Maintain my coping skills and eliminate any anger intensifiers such as the use of alcohol or drugs, caffeine, lack of sleep, and the like.

- Use humor to defuse my stress, what is called "gallows humor"…making fun even in the worst situations. Have the ability to view things with a twist. Humor helps me undo the knots of negative emotions. It gives me a breather from my worries. I watch the comedy channel or listen to comedy channels on Sirius radio. I read humorous books and watch funny movies. Smiling and laughter help.

- Allow my training to "kick in." Focus on what must be done in the given situation. Be flexible and choose the best strategy that meets the needs of the situation. If one technique does not work, then try another one. "Adapt and overcome" is my motto. Increased control and preparedness makes me more resilient and better able to adapt flexibly to challenging situations.

- Ask myself "What is my plan if this happens again?"

Quotable Quotes

"Since I have gone through mindfulness training I try to just break down each moment into the space of a breath, so that I will feel whatever I am feeling. I just tell myself that it is ok whatever I feel. Not judge the feeling as to whether it is good or bad, or ask myself do I want to feel this way. I know that the feelings will pass. It will pass as long as I keep focusing on my breathing."

"Since I learned to use my Relaxation Response, I am able to relax my body from head to toe and then focus on my breathing. Every time I breath out, I repeat the word "Calm" or "One," or sometimes say a prayer. When other thoughts enter my mind, I disregard them by saying "Oh well!" I view my thoughts like an ocean wave that will continue to rise up and make a wave and then watch it leave. This took some practice since it is like a 'mental muscle' that needs exercise in order to become habitually automatic."

"It's hard to explain. Since the trauma experience settled down, I am getting along with people better, and I do not get as angry as I used to. The way I look at things is different. I don't seem as afraid of or worry about things that I used to be afraid of or worry about. I pay more attention and spend more time with the people I love. Many of the beliefs about life that I used to hold don't seem to fit with who I am now."

"Taking these Steps to Emotional Fitness will lead to a happier and healthier me and lead to better relationships with those I care for."

"Remember: those who fail to plan ahead may plan to fail."

In summary, whenever I experience intense negative emotions I can become an "emotional detective" by:

- Taking my emotional temperature and spot-checking my emotional state

- Naming and taming my feelings

- Locating and deconditioning intense feelings

- Increasing my trigger awareness

- Tolerating and accepting intense feelings ("Ride the emotional wave")

- Be mindful and stay centered

- Get grounded, if need be

- Use relaxation and tactical breathing

- Change my self-talk

- Practice containment and compartmentalize (put things on the "back burner")

- Use SOS skills (Slow down, Orient, Self-check). Engage in Opposite Actions

- Use humor

- Share my "story" and what I am feeling with others I trust to be supportive

By doing these things I can have a "corrective emotional experience."

ACTION #42

I made the choice/decision to stay out of my way emotionally and be very careful about what I tell myself, my "self-talk." Self-talk includes the words in my head that can seem like a conversation with myself. Sometimes it may be in the form of images or mental movies of events. These streams of words and images that describe and interpret events can direct my actions and influence my feelings. This stream of self-talk seems automatic, as if having a life of it's own. When such self-talk is repeated over and over, it becomes a "mental habit" and is ingrained. Such self-talk can misinterpret events and distort events and make situations worse than they are and prove counterproductive.

Useful Information

A key to strengthening one's resilience is the ability to engage in less negative thinking. There are significant benefits if individuals can generate three to four positive thoughts for every negative thought (3 or 4:1 ratio of positive to negative thoughts). The goal is not to eliminate completely negative thoughts. Negative thoughts can be motivating. The key is to tip the balance of positive to negative thinking. Individuals are not at the mercy of their emotions.

I can become a "thought detective." For example, I can learn to ask myself the following *Hinge Questions* on a regular basis:

- "When I am feeling down, I can ask oneself—what message am I giving myself? I can stop and look for the message I am giving myself."

- "When I say this to myself, I tend to feel..."

- "How can I learn to watch out for the 'self-attacks' of what I say to myself."

- "What am I thinking that makes me feel...?"

- "What is another way of thinking that could help me manage my emotions better?"

- "How can I plan ahead to anticipate situations that are likely to trigger these emotions?"

- "How do these feelings affect the way I see things? Am I being prejudiced about how I see myself, only focused on the negative?"

- "If I am feeling completely undervalued, unappreciated and unsupported by others, what is the data (evidence) for these beliefs? What can I do to change this situation? What specific things can I do to improve my relationships?"

- "Do I do things to try and avoid unwanted thoughts, images, and memories of traumatic events?"

- "Do I consume alcohol, drugs; engage in risky behaviors and avoidance to cope with specific memories, symptoms and bad feelings?"

- "If I do these things, then what is the price and toll I and others pay?"

- "If this happened to someone else, would I come to the same conclusions? What advice would I offer?"

- "What can I do to improve the Quality of My Life?"

- "Is there a way I could reframe this trauma, distress, as a challenge?"

- "Can I think of an example that does not fit my belief that I am X?"

- "Can I think of something that would make my happiness grow?"

How To: Talk Back to My Brain Differently

The part of your brain that is involved with emotions and memories is the *Amygdala*. The Amygdala is the brain's "gatekeeper" for incoming emotional memories. Traumatic memories can stay trapped in the Amygdala and can continue to trigger frightening images and strong emotions. Such emotional memories can be triggered even when no real threats are present and act like "faulty smoke detectors." The Amygdala can "hijack" your emotions and put your prefrontal cortex (the front part of your brain which is in charge of self-regulation) "offline". By learning to "talk back to your brain" you can help the Amygdala "loosen its grip" and you can learn to "put the brakes on" when you need to. You can learn to RE-balance your nervous system. You can teach your brain to separate the past from the present. You can learn how to control your emotions and cravings and bring your "learning brain" (prefrontal cortex) on-line and *override* your "survival brain" (Amygdala and sub cortex).

You may mistake the movies of your mind for reality. Your body cannot tell the difference between what is actually happening and what you are imagining. You cannot expect a different set of feelings when you use the same self-talk. Your body is reacting to the frightening images and your scary expectations as if they were real. You need to calm yourself down and come back down to earth and check out what is happening.

ACTION #43

I need to *engage in non-negative thinking*. I choose to engage in ways of thinking that help me become more resilient. I am *proud* of what I have accomplished and I can use the lessons learned to take care of myself, my buddies and my loved ones. I can help others and myself "win the war within" and address any "invisible wounds." I can share positive coping skills directly with others.

Useful Information

The "5 C's" of "stress hardiness," as identified by Salvatore Maddi and Suzanne Kobasa, consist of:

C—Commitment—What brings purpose and passion to my life? Do I get fully involved, evidence vital engagement, a zest for life, set new goals and undertake steps to meet them? Do I maintain an ongoing engagement with potentially stressful situations? Instead of "turning off," I can "tune in."

C—Challenge—Do I interpret difficult situations as opportunities for change and learning? Do I view challenges as an invitation to learn and master new skills and make new connections?"

C— Control—Do I focus most of my time and energy on factors over which I have influence? Or am I still waiting for others to change their behavior first? Do I have a sense of personal agency that I am the 'Captain of my own fate', an 'orchestrator of my life'?" Do I feel that the locus of control is within me?

C—Confidence—Do I have a sense of self-efficacy that I can meet this challenge? Do I have the ability and confidence to make do with whatever is at hand in order to solve this problem? Do I have the ability to improvise and evidence ingenuity?

C—Connected—Do I have others ("Recovery Capital") whom I can call upon for assistance?

Remember that calm thinking and coping with stress are learned skills that become strengthened through repeated practice.

Summary of Emotional Fitness Strategies

All situations you encounter during post-deployment or following a traumatic event can be broken into four components that can be summarized using the imagery of the framework of a clock. Consider:

12 o'clock represents triggers or activating events, both external and internal events. This is what someone does or does not do- some event that occurs. This perception

will likely trigger some emotional reactions. Some Triggers may be Internal like a flashback or perception of a threat or a craving.

3 o'clock represents a set of *primary and secondary emotions.* This is how you may feel immediately (for example, anxious, depressed, angry, and the like). These Primary Emotions may in turn contribute to Secondary Emotions. You may feel humiliated then get angry, or you may feel depressed about not being able to control your fears. A "chain reaction" of emotions may be set in motion and cascade.

6 o'clock represents the accompanying *thoughts* and *self-talk* or what individuals say to themselves in the heat of the moment and the deeply held *beliefs* ("mental icebergs") that drive out-of-proportion emotional reactions. This covers your expectations and attributions (causative explanations). For example, to get from being angry to becoming aggressive, you need to believe that the other person slighted you or upset you "on purpose." This belief or self-statement contributes to further distress. It is not just events, but how we view such events or what we "tell ourselves" that influence how we react.

9 o'clock represents what you do (behaviors and actions) and how others respond.

To summarize:

- 12 o'clock = External and internal triggers ("What started this?")

- 3 o'clock = Primary and secondary emotions ("What am I feeling?")

- 6 o'clock = Automatic thoughts, self-talk, expectations, beliefs ("What am I thinking?")

- 9 o'clock = Behavioral reactions and responses of others ("What am I doing?")

These four components may operate and become a *vicious cycle.* Sometimes you may go from 12 o'clock (triggers) to 9 o'clock (behavioral reactions) and then to 3 o'clock (feelings) and then to 6 o'clock (self-talk) which influences how you view future 12 o'clock events. Sometimes you can generate further stress so this can become a "vicious cycle."

Consider how you now attempt to break such vicious cycles in your life. What are the events (12 o'clock) prompting your reactions? What are your interpretations, assumptions and thoughts (6 o'clock) about these events? Can you find better ways to break the cycle? Can you view perceived "threats" (12 o'clock) as "problems-to-be-solved"? Can you control, tolerate, accept, share your emotions (3 o'clock)? Can you change your self-talk (6 o'clock)? Can you behave differently and elicit different reactions from others (9 o'clock)? As you can see, there are many entry-points to break the vicious cycle. Doing these things will help you become more resilient.

ACTION #44

Here are other examples of ways to experience positive emotions and manage negative emotions and improve my *emotional fitness*. (Please email these suggestions to *examples@roadmaptoresilience.org*)

_____

_____

_____

_____

Thinking (Cognitive) Fitness

"Resilience is a mindset." (A mindset is the set of assumptions and expectations that we hold about ourselves and others that guide our actions.)

"Resilient individuals use practical wisdom and are psychologically flexible, recognizing changing situational demands and adapting accordingly."

"Resilient individuals rework their 'trauma stories' into 'healing stories' and integrate them into their autobiographical memories and place them alongside other life experiences."

Thinking fitness is the ability to be psychologically flexible and mentally agile, to notice and avoid 'Thinking Traps', to be an effective problem-solver, optimistic, and produce a "healing story" that contributes to one's *resilience*.

ACTION #45

I focus on being *flexible* and adjust to changing demands. I can learn *not to* try and control things that I *cannot* control.

Useful Information

Charles Darwin observed: "It is not the strongest of the species who survives, nor the most intelligent, but the one most responsive to change."

The need for cognitive flexibility is also highlighted in the Serenity Prayer that is used in Alcoholics Anonymous.

"God, grant me the serenity to accept the things I cannot change; courage to change the things I can; and the wisdom to know the difference."

How To: Steps to Becoming More Psychologically Flexible: Adapt and Overcome

1. Recognize and adapt to various fluctuating situational demands. Avoid "change blindness."

2. Change mindsets and perspectives and accompanying behavioral repertoires, when needed.

3. Be aware of thoughts and feelings in the present.

4. Shift intentional focus from the past or the future to the present.

5. Find alternative routes toward desired goals. Engage in pathways thinking.

6. Organize and prioritize strategies and actions that fit the situation.

7. Be open to and accepting of emotional experiences and tolerate distress and frustration.

8. Be willing to engage in difficult situations and undertake challenging tasks that have uncertainty and risks.

9. Persist and show grit and determination.

10. View failures as "learning opportunities" and *not* as end-points. Diagnose failures so you can see potential obstacles and setbacks coming on and can head them off. Trouble-shoot situations. Welcome a healthy relationship with failure. Conduct after-action debriefings.

11. Maintain a balance among important life domains.

12. Organize a life built around meaningful beliefs and values.

Quotable Quotes

"Psychological flexibility involves being clear about one's values and mindful of one's thoughts and feelings and acting in accord with your values."

"I live by the 'F WORD' and that word is 'Flexible.'"

"We must let go of the life we have planned, so as to accept the one that is waiting for us."

—Joseph Campbell

"When you come home from deployment or after a disaster you have to learn to fit in. Find a way to fit in."

"I can make the choice to stay out of my way emotionally. Remember, there is no situation so bad that by my own efforts I cannot make it worse."

ACTION #46

I use constructive thinking and my problem-solving skills. Problem-solving is about finding solutions to challenges. I can see things in a new light. Generate multiple options and alternative solutions. Weigh the pros and cons of each alternative solution. I foresee future problems and losses and take preventable steps before the stressors reveal themselves. I can mentally and behaviorally rehearse possible actions beforehand. Imagery rehearsal is like a free ride, it provides an opportunity to see things differently through a new set of lenses, anticipating challenges and potential obstacles. *Mental rehearsal* or vividly picturing in my mind the situation as it is expected to unfold and my problem-solving steps help move me from thoughts to actions.

Useful Information

Things to keep in mind that when it comes to *problem-solving*.

1. View the problem as a "challenge" and use the six P's

   a. **Problem**—problem definition—define the problem in behavioral language so another person can understand. Define the problem narrowly and specifically.

   b. **Purpose**—define goals in a brief and uncomplicated manner. Set "smart" goal statements. (See Action #47)

   c. **Plan**—solution generation—use brainstorming to generate at least three possible alternatives for yourself; brainstorm and suspend judgment at first. Quantity counts and quality comes later.

   d. **Pick**—select one solution. If it doesn't work, try another solution. Stay calm and remind oneself to work at it. Use calming strategies if needed. Choose a solution that all parties agree is best, after thoughtful discussion of the pros and cons, costs and benefits.

   e. **Predict**—anticipate and identify possible obstacles and address such potential roadblocks ahead of time.

   f. **Pat oneself on the back**—evaluate the outcome and reward oneself for your efforts. What was learned?

      "Challenges can be stepping stones or stumbling blocks. It's just a matter of how you view them."

2. Change one's relationship to the problem. Ask myself "Is it my problem, or someone else's problem, or a joint problem?

3. Work on solving the problem and assume future solutions by using "future talk." What is future talk? It includes expressions such as *so far* or *as yet*.

> "*So far* things have not gone right."
> "I have not found a way to stay out of trouble, *as yet*."

Future talk tells others and oneself that there are potential solutions to be found down the road.

4. Mentally and behaviorally rehearse, "try out" actions and solutions *ahead of time*. I can cope ahead by imagining the situation as vividly as possible. I can imagine myself in the situation, not watching the situation. Imagine the scene in the present tense, not in the future or past. Now rehearse coping more effectively, envisioning, "What would I do and say?" Athletes often use such imagery-based coping ahead strategies to improve their performance.

ACTION #47

Identify doable, achievable, observable, measurable goals and plans. The goals I choose should be concrete, and not abstract, relevant, meaningful and important for me and others like my spouse to work on. I need to define my goals in small steps to increase the likelihood of success and to develop a sense of accomplishment. I can break large problems into smaller ones. I can focus my energy and concentrate my attention on a few important goals. I can prepare ahead of time for stressful events. I can also develop back-up plans to achieve my goals and be able to follow-through. I can ask myself,

> "*What is one thing, even if it is a little thing, which I can accomplish today that will help me move in the direction that I want to go?*"

It is important to state goals in *positive action terms*, rather than in words of what should not occur. For example, "not shouting" should become "please speak calmly." There is a need to track progress toward achieving such goals. Keep in mind that "*small steps can lead to big changes.*" It is like throwing a small stone into a pond and watching a small splash generate ripples that have an expanding effect.

Use *Solution Talk* that focuses on the language of what works, rather than on the language of what is wrong. It puts the spotlight on discovering and implementing solutions in the here and now with the goal of improving the future. *Solution Talk* includes "how" and "what" questions.

> "*How would I like things to be?*"

> "*How have I handled challenges/problems like this in the past?*"

"How did I do that?"

"How could I repeat (recycle, revisit) my skills and use them now?"

"What can I bring forward and use in this situation?"

"What can I do differently?"

"What is working? Can I do more of this?"

"What is a first step that I can take?"

Keep in mind that I need to make "S.M.A.R.T. Goals."

- **S**pecific goals—establish targeted goals in behavioral terms of what I wish to achieve. The stated goals should answer, "What, When, Where, How often and With Whom?"

- **M**easurable goals—should be something that I can assess relative to where I began (my baseline), or what I am doing or not doing *now*. I need to be able to measure or count my behavior in some way and track progress.

- **A**chievable goals—these should be doable objectives. Start small and then make goals gradually more challenging, as compared to setting unrealistic goals. Focus on initiating or starting *new behaviors*, rather than on trying to eliminate negative behaviors. Frame my goals in "positive terms." It is easier to increase, as opposed to reduce or stop or eliminate "bad" behaviors.

- **R**ealistic—be optimistic, but do not overshoot my goals. Anticipate barriers and what I will do if I encounter roadblocks or obstacles. Formulate "If . . . then" and "Whenever I encounter . . . I will" plans. Don't be a perfectionist. Learn from setbacks. Set goals that are important and relevant to my life, really meaningful and consistent with my values. Values orient people towards goals. *Prioritize* my goals and start off with those that are most doable, so I have the best chance of success.

- **T**ime-limited goals—should have an end-point in order to keep me motivated. Set a realistic deadline and a doable time frame for achieving my short-term, intermediate and long-term goals. Share this "game plan" with someone I trust and make a public commitment statement. Remember, "Think Big, but Act Small." Every big goal is accomplished in small steps. Reinforce my efforts along the way. It is not the outcome, but the effort that contributes to *resilience*.

New Year's resolutions usually do not work. Setting and sharing "S.M.A.R.T. Goals" have a better chance of working. What are the "goals behind the goals" and how can they be achieved? Finally, two different sets of goals have been iden-tified by Carol Dweck. (Dweck, 2012) One is called *mastery* goals and the other is called *performance* goals. The *mastery* goals are established by oneself and reflect intrinsic motivation, engaging in an activity for its own sake. Individuals are more likely to demonstrate greater persistence and accept mistakes as part of learning, ask for help, demonstrate curiosity when setting one's performance standards. In contrast, performance-based goals, whereby the objectives and standards of performance are established and evaluated by others, are more likely to lead to giving up, fear of being outperformed by others, fear of mistakes and lower motivation to achieve. When establishing goals, it is better to employ self-established *mastery* goals.

ACTION #48

I establish *realistic expectations* and learn to give up and to disengage from blocked, unattainable and insoluble goals. I check my expectations against the expectations of my family members. I ask myself the following *Hinge Questions:*

> *"What is the smallest change I can make in this area?"*

> *"What is one thing I can accomplish today that can help me achieve my short-term goal of . . . ?"*

I recall how I have achieved my goals in the past and apply those skills now. I can ask myself "what" and "how" questions.

- "What did I do in the past?"

- "How did I do that?"

- "What do others do to handle this situation?"

- "How do they pull it off?"

- "What do other people see as my strengths and how can I use these strengths to handle this situation?"

- "What is it that I can do differently to change the situation?"

- "What is one thing that I can accomplish today that can help me achieve my short-term goal of . . . ?"

- "How can I adapt myself to this situation?"

- "How can I avoid high-risk situations in the future?"

ACTION #49

I learn to look at events in a different way and in a new light. I can learn to use the following types of statements:

"Rather than"
"Yes...but"
"Without becoming"
"If...then"
"Before...I will"
"Whenever"
"In spite of"
"On the one hand *and* on the other hand"

- Use *rather than* statements:
  "I will learn to (choose, accept, plan), *rather than* fight (flee, avoid)."
  "I would prefer to become a 'better person', *rather than* a 'bitter person'."

- Use *yes...but* statements:
  "*Yes*, it is true that I have hurt others, drank too much, *but* now I am working hard..., using my coping tool kit."

- Use *without becoming* statements:
  "I am going to get help *without becoming* overwhelmed, upset, avoidant."

- Use *if...then* statements:
  "*If* I run into my drinking buddies, (have flashbacks, nightmares), *then* I will find someone I trust to share this with or go for help."

- Use *before...I will* statements:
  "*Before I* do something that will make my situation worse, (give into my cravings), *I will* ride them out like a wave (think through the consequences)."

- Use *whenever* statements:
  "*Whenever* I find myself feeling down, I will engage in the opposite action (work to tolerate, change, and control my emotions, exercise)."

- Use *in spite of* statements:
  "I can share what I accomplished (learned) with people who are close to me *in spite of* the bad things that have happened. (Tell the rest of the story of my survival skills)."

- Use *and* statements:
  "*On the one hand* I feel (negative emotions), but *on the other hand* I am still able to keep going, finding meaning *and* at the same time feel

pride." I am feeling down on myself/my situation *and* at the *same time* I can also see hope (remember how I handled this in the past).

Remember that small changes in language and story-telling can open new possibilities for future change.

ACTION #50

I use *hope* by establishing and pursuing doable positive goals and use my abilities to achieve them. I use my "hidden strengths" and "buried treasures," to survive and thrive, "in spite of" the great odds that I wouldn't succeed. I strengthen my self-efficacy or my belief in my ability to cope successfully with difficulties. I translate my "know how" into coping tools.

Hope is a powerful antidote to helplessness and despair.

An interesting way psychotherapists nurture hope is to use what is called the "miracle question." (Metcalf, 2004).

> *"Imagine when you go to sleep at night, a miracle happens and when you wake up the next morning, things are different in a good way. Since you are sleeping, you do not know that a miracle has happened and that whatever problems you are working on has been solved. What do you suppose you will notice different the next morning that will tell you there has been a miracle? What exactly would have changed when you wake up that would alert you that a miracle has indeed happened? How would you be thinking and behaving differently? What would other folks notice? Now, what might you do to reach these goals? What small initial steps can you take to get there? What does this tell you about your strengths, your coping abilities, your survival skills, your abilities to live your 'in spite of' story?"*

On a Scale of 1 to 10, how hopeful are you that things can improve in your life, with 1 being not at all hopeful and 10 being most hopeful. What needs to happen for you to feel one point closer to your goal?

Hinge Questions:

- "What have you done to cope and survive in the past?"

- "What has kept you going?"

- "Is there anything you have done in the past that worked that you can use now?"

- "What would need to happen to help you be more hopeful about the future?"

- "What keeps you going in difficult and challenging times?"

- "Whom can you rely on during difficult times?"

- "What resources do you possess that can give you hope for the future?"

- "Do you have a vision of your future?"

- "What do you imagine you will be doing in one year from now? Five years from now?"

- "What do you want your future to look like?"

- "Are you taking steps to accomplish these things?"

- "How could you get yourself to the point of initiating some small, but meaningful changes?"

- "Whom can you share this game plan with?"

- "How will you know if you are making progress?"

Remember: *hope begets hope.*

Looking for the positives allow people to gain a sense of control and mastery and help them restore their sense of self-esteem, and foster a hopeful outlook. As we will see in Action #62 and Action #65, there is value in learning to use the language of hope and becoming. Think hopefully.

Quotable Quotes

"I view my distress not as evidence of mental disorders, but as part of the human condition."

"Bad things happen to me, but good outcomes often follow."

"Remember that cracks let the light shine through."

"I can see my old self through the eyes of my new self."

"I can shift my perspective and share my story of survival, and my story of change."

"Life is not about how to survive the storm, but how to dance in the rain."

"I should not let what I cannot do interfere with what I can do."

"How I choose to be today is not predetermined by who I was yesterday."

"I remind myself that trauma and distress can push people to develop in positive ways, to develop new levels of psychological resilience, develop new survival skills, greater self-knowledge, self-appreciation, increased empathy and a more broad and complex view of life."

"Trauma can result in growth."

"I stay motivated in tough times by keeping my personal and career goals in mind."

ACTION #51

Optimism has been defined as generalized expectancies for desirable future outcomes. I can be realistically optimistic and goal-directed, but not take on more than I can handle. I can maintain a hopeful attitude, and have a future orientation, imagine good outcomes and engage in future life planning. I can choose to pursue optimism, instead of pessimism.

Pessimists tend to think, *"It's all my fault. I mess up everything that I do and it is the story of my life."* Pessimists are more likely to mentally check out and put their head in the sand.

I can choose to pursue realistic optimism, instead of pessimism.

Realistic optimists have a habitual way of exploring events. They see the negative, but do not dwell on it, nor over generalize about the positive. They have the ability to size up a situation dispassionately, while still staying open to future possibilities and new ideas and experiences.

> *"The Pessimist complains about the wind;*
> *The Optimist expects it to change;*
> *The Realistic Optimist adjusts the sails"*
> —William Arthur Ward

Useful Information

Optimists, as compared to pessimists, have better individual and interpersonal well-being, use more effective coping strategies, have better health and are better liked and supported, and make a higher salary. Optimism confers resilience to stressful events. Rather than cling to the past, optimists use the past as teaching lessons and become the future. They believe that the future is not something that just happens, but something they can help create. As the song goes in the musical South Pacific, I can learn to become a "cock-eyed optimist."

Where do you fall on the dimension of *optimism* to *pessimism* and can you train yourself to think and act in ways that optimists do? It might not be easy at first to change from a pessimistic to an optimistic mindset, but the outcome is well worth the effort. Consider the following chart and determine where you fit.

OPTIMISTS	PESSIMISTS
Expect *good things* to happen to them.	Expect *bad things* to happen to them.
See things in the best light.	Tend to attribute negative events to personal and permanent factors ("This is out of my control." "It is not going to get better."), and are therefore less likely to take actions to change it.
Bad stuff is time and context limited. ("I am going through a rough patch. I possess good and resourceful qualities I can use.").	Think that bad stuff is out of one's own control and feel a lack of personal ability and resourcefulness to change things ("I'm such a loser.").
Focus less on the negative aspects of their experiences (distress and symptoms).	Escape adversity by wishful thinking: drawn into temporary distractions that don't help to solve the problem.
Tend to attribute the causes of negative events to temporary, changeable and specific factors.	Doubt that their goals can be attained and may withdraw effort, stop prematurely or may never really start. Less persistent.
Expect good outcomes even when things are hard. Continue trying even when the going gets tough.	More likely to "stick their head in the sand" and ignore threats to well-being.
Engage in proactive (future-planning) coping. Use problem-solving coping when there is something to be done. More likely to seek out relevant information.	Use passive and avoidant coping responses.
Take active steps to ensure positive outcomes in the future. Work to prevent a stressor from arising.	More likely to drop out of training and treatment programs.
More likely to engage in exercise and make efforts to reduce risks, safeguarding their health. Do things to make good things happen.	People are more likely to reject someone who has a negative outlook and who expresses negative expectations.

OPTIMISTS	PESSIMISTS
Work harder and more effectively on relationships resulting in a large, more supportive social network.	More likely to give up and withdraw.
Have decreased autonomic arousal, lower levels of anxiety and depression and respond more favorably to medical procedures.	Tend to become more anxious and depressed.

Can optimism have drawbacks? Being an optimist may have a down-side. For example, optimists may undertake too many tasks and spread their resources too thin. Being an optimist may contribute to problem gambling where positive expectations and persistence may be counterproductive. Optimists are less likely to disengage from gambling- even after experiencing gambling losses. Optimists may refrain from providing constructive criticism and hold the "false hope" that things will improve on their own and undermine the motivation to seek improvements. Unfounded optimism is *not* helpful. Beware of the "Tyranny of positive attitudes."

There is a need to be a *realistic optimist*. Remember that:

"When things get tough, the tough get going."

How To: Nurture an Optimistic Outlook

1. Identify and write down times in the past in which you were performing at your best. What did you do (and not do)? How did others react? How did that make you feel? What did you think (and not think)? Be specific.

2. List your personal strengths. What do other folks see in you? Write these down and give specific examples. No fluff—just the hard facts.

3. Keep a list of things you are grateful for—(see Action #30 and Seligman, 2006).

ACTION #52

I have *confidence* in my ability to bring about positive outcomes and have a sense of personal control, that is, I hold the belief that things can change for the better and that I have the ability to bring about such changes. I focus on my abilities, my "islands of competence," not on my disabilities. "Biology is *not* destiny." Never lose sight of strength and virtues that reside within me.

A sign that I am gaining confidence and developing resilience is that I can use "I" statements to compliment myself such as:

- "I decided to . . . "

- "I now realize that . . . "

- "I have tested out my hunches . . . "

- "I learn from the past. How have I coped in the past? This gives me confidence and hope which is the spark for change. Hope reminds me that the future can bring new possibilities."

- "I approach challenges and adversities with a positive attitude which gives me a chance for success. If I approach the situation with a negative attitude this predestines the outcome of failure and defeat. These negative expectations become self-fulfilling prophecies."

- "I not only can recognize my strengths and positive qualities, I can own them."

- "I can notice positive changes."

- "I can be supportive and flexible with myself when I fail or fall short of meeting my expectations and standards."

- "I nurture myself and continually need to remind myself of how far I have come."

- "I can *compliment* myself when I do something worthwhile and feel I *deserve* it."

Useful Information

I can make a list of challenging experiences that I have overcome in my life and describe how I handled them. What did I do while deployed that I can now use in handling stressors in my civilian life? How do others (my war buddies, family members, members of my racial/cultural group) handle challenges? What can I learn from them?

ACTION #53

I engage in "benefit-finding." I can identify positive outcomes of an otherwise negative experience. I usually search for the "silver lining." For me, the glass is half-full, rather than being half-empty. I can put a "positive spin" on events; reframe negative experiences in a more positive way. I can find unexpected benefits. For example, I can complete the following sentences:

As a result of this experience I can ask myself the following *Hinge Questions*:

- "Has anything positive come out of this experience for me and others?"

- "I am now . . . "

- "I now know that . . . "

- "I am better prepared to . . . "

- "I now see new . . . "

- "I can now better appreciate . . . "

- "I have prepared myself, so I can now . . . "

- "I have learned some valuable things about myself and about my buddies, (family members) that I would not have learned any other way, such as . . ."

- "This was a test of my manhood (womanhood) and what I learned was . . ."

- "I am more resilient in the following ways . . . "

Useful Information

Survivors of a disaster who reported benefits within four to six weeks were less likely to be diagnosed with PTSD three years later and showed less distress than survivors who did not report any benefits. The perception of signs of growth played a valuable role in later adjustment.

Benefit-finding has been related to positive changes in neuroendocrine functioning in the decreased production of the stress hormone cortisol and lower mortality rates among those suffering from AIDS. Benefit-finding slowed down the growth rate of cells that contribute to disease progression.

Benefit-finding also leads to increased social supports and to the use of adaptive cognitive strategies among HIV patients and with patients with multiple sclerosis.

Quotable Quotes

"Going through this taught me that I did not know how strong I was until I confronted these things. I realized I could call upon my own reserves and I got to be stronger. I realize if I got through this, I can cope with anything."

"I am wiser (stronger) as a result of this experience."

"I am better prepared for whatever comes along."

"I am less afraid of change."

"I am better now at helping others."

"This brought us all together."

"I learned I am my brother's keeper."

"I can take responsibility for my actions and I can engage in recovery thinking."

ACTION #54

I engage in "benefit-remembering" by "looking backward in order to move forward." I can write down and share with significant others how I have gotten through past stressful events. I can ask others who have done well, what has helped them. I can listen and try these things. I can figure out what has proven helpful for me and others in the past that is likely to prove helpful now and in the future. I can ask myself the following *Hinge Questions*:

- "How has dealing with this situation made me a stronger person?"

- "How can I learn something from this situation?"

- "How can I share this knowledge with someone I hold dear?"

- "Is there a blessing in disguise to be found?"

Quotable Quotes

"I can stop repeating the same old mistakes when I am really upset. I now have a new game plan and the confidence to try it out. What worked in the past that I can use?"

"I can stop repeating the negative messages that I received from others. Remember my survival skills, my 'in spite of' story."

ACTION #55

I engage in *downward* comparisons which mean that I can compare my present situation and condition with others who are less fortunate or worse off. I can also create a "worse world scenario" of what might have happened. Engaging in downward comparisons can contribute to "positive feelings" because things "could have been worse. At least, I am able to . . . " and " I still have . . . " This can result in my feeling somewhat better off and grateful for what I do have.

As a result of this experience:

"Compared to others, do I feel I am in a better or worse situation?"

"Was it as bad as it could be or could it have been worse?"

"Has anything that has happened made me feel particularly lucky?"

"Is this experience as negative as I would have imagined before going through it?"

Quotable Quotes

"I think about others and how it could have been worse."

"I am now able to focus on the fact that it happened."

"I see new possibilities and goals to work on."

"My view of what is important in life has changed."

"I can let the past just be the past. I am no longer interested in reliving what happened."

"I can tell my story like an objective reporter and not get emotionally overwhelmed."

"I realize I can tell my story in broad strokes and do not have to go into all the nitty-gritty details."

"I realize I can tell my story and I will not fall apart."

ACTION #56

I make a detailed list of my positive experiences of my military or civilian life and share this with significant others. I go on a "meaning-making mission". When meaning is found, I do not set aside the search for meaning, rather this is an ongoing process. The journey continues.

Useful Information

Traumatic experiences can clear the way for meaning-making, a sense of purpose that we would not have found otherwise. The healing process forges new meaning that can make way for growth. Resilient individuals tend to be highly generative and try to make the world a better place. They often serve as volunteers, mentors and political activists. They re-engage life.

Consider that in the sixth century, St. Benedict founded his monastic order on Mount Cassino, Italy in order to help individuals cope more effectively with trauma and illness. The organizing principle of the monastic order was "Ora et Labora" (Pray and work). The sense of having a *mission* was viewed in the sixth century, as well as now, as essential to building resilience"(as cited by Nathan Ainspan, Walter Penk and Dolores Little).

Quotable Quotes

"We survived and we have a chance to live and we are choosing life."

"God has given me a second chance."

"I survived for a purpose, to help prevent this from happening again."

"I am no longer willing to be defined by my victimization."

"I moved from being a victim to becoming a survivor and even a thriver."

"I can make a gift of my pain and loss and share it with others so they can be wiser and better prepared."

"I try to pass along the knowledge I have gained through my experiences."

"I now know God."

"Recognizing the fragility of life, you can refocus on what's important to you, and not waste time on things that aren't."

ACTION #57

I create a sense of purpose that results from this trauma experience; a survivor's mission that nurtures my "will to live." I make a "gift" of what I have learned to others. Be altruistic which is a selfless concern for the welfare of others. I have a motivation to help others without reward or recognition.

Useful Information

There is a strong link between enriching the lives of others and one's own sense of self-worth, well-being and resilience. There is much benefit to the person who contributes to others. People who work for greater political and religious causes are happier and more positive about life. Such public commitment frees them from individual concerns.

When you open your heart to other people to listen and care about them, it changes the way you look at the world. Acts of altruism release "feel good hormones" called endorphins, and as noted, are described as a "helper's high."

> *"Do good—be good—our attitudes and beliefs often follow from our behaviors, rather than precede them. If you engage in volunteer behaviors or other altruistic activities, you are likely to see yourself as a caring person."*

Quotable Quotes

> *"It is one of the most beneficial compensations of life that no man can sincerely try to help another without helping himself."*
> —Ralph Waldo Emerson

> *"I want to write a new chapter. I want to be the author of my recovery."*

> *"Be prepared—I want to reduce the risk of my revictimization and help others."*

> *"I am like a Phoenix rising from the ashes."*

> *"I know I am feeling overwhelmed, but I have felt this way before and it always passes. I do not have to respond to my feelings. I am getting better at fighting off my depression and not giving into it. I refuse to be revictimized by my past. I can move on."*

A Holocaust survivor who grew up to become a human rights expert, observed:

> *"I knew I would never quite liberate myself from the past and that it would forever shape my life. But I also knew that I would not permit it to have a debilitating or destructive effect on the new life I was about to begin. My past would inspire my future and give it meaning."*
> —Thomas Buergenthal, 2009

ACTION #58

I pursue life-affirming and uplifting activities that enable me to develop a sense of purpose and meaning in my life. I give back and engage in "pass forward" activities.

Useful Information

Many returning service members who have been transformed by their military experiences report such benefits as the development of self-discipline, increasing their stress tolerance and self-confidence, broadening their perspective on life, changing life priorities, improving relationships and increasing their sense of spirituality. Some even report a type of posttraumatic growth (PTG). As noted, PTG can co-exist with PTSD symptoms and post traumatic stress can act as a catalyst or engine for the development of PTG.

Quotable Quotes

"As a result of my deployment I am more alive and aware at a pure psychological level than I had been for a long time."

"I carry with me harrowing stories and memories, but also hopeful memories and pride in what we accomplished. I served my country."

"To live is to suffer. To survive is to find meaning in the suffering. The ability to see something good in adversity is the central trait needed by all of us."

"The way in which a man accepts his fate and all the suffering it entails, the way in which he takes up his cross, gives him ample opportunity, even under the most difficult circumstances, to add a deeper meaning to his life, remaining brave, dignified and unselfish."

—Viktor Frankl, 1985

"Bad things happened. I can't change what happened, but I can try to put my life back together and move on and hopefully help other people who had the same experience get better."

ACTION #59

From my trauma experiences, I have learned several important life lessons. I can now get involved with others to improve society, reduce violence, and the like.

Author's note: As a result of trauma social movements, political actions and organizations have been developed (e.g., Mothers Against Drunk Driving, Physicians for Social Responsibility, Nuremberg Trials, South African Truth and Reconciliation Commission, and the Melissa Institute for Violence Prevention of which I am the Research Director (Please visit www.melissainstitute.org).

Is there some mission, some cause, some group of family or friends that you can engage with that will give purpose and help bolster your resilience? Consider the following *Hinge Questions:*

- *"I survived for a purpose which is . . . "*

- *"I am no longer willing to be defined by my accident/injury/ victimization/trauma experience, I am now . . . "*

- "I now devote myself to . . . "

- "I can make a 'gift' of my experience by doing . . . "

Quotable Quotes

"Like an infected wound, the only way to stop an infection is to open it up and clean it out. It might sting, but in the long run, it is the only way to heal."

"Our life is what our thoughts make of it."

—Marcus Aurelius

"I can identify my maladaptive mindset and begin to change it."

"I can develop and cultivate a growth-oriented voice and resilient mindset."

"I can integrate the traumatic experience into the totality of the rest of my life-story."

"I can remember that trauma is only part of my life-story, rather than the defining aspect."

ACTION #60

I "mentalize"—increase my awareness of my thinking processes and my self-talk in the here and now and monitor, alter them, as needed. I have the ability to separate the past from the present and become an outside observer of my own thinking processes. I can think about and evaluate my own thoughts and actions as if I were observing them in a detached manner like an outsider. I try to see myself as others would see me. I can consider the pros and cons of my thinking processes. What are the benefits and negative consequences, both short-term and long-term of my continuing to think the ways I think? I can put my stress system back in *balance*. I can bring up and call online the front part of my brain that helps me take charge.

- "I was about to do . . . "

- "I can notice, catch, interrupt . . . "

- "I can think through the consequences . . . "

- "It is as if I have you on my shoulder guiding me . . . "

- "I have learned to ask myself the questions I usually discuss with my therapist."

Quotable Quotes

"I can learn to talk to my brain differently."

"It is like I have a remote control TV channel selector. I have the ability to tune into a 'pleasant event' channel when I am depressed; a 'time out' channel when I am angry, a 'social problem-solving' channel, a 'cheerleading' channel, a 'facing my fear' channel."

"I am able to think about the trauma, but recognize that I am not in danger."

"I can train my body to turn off my alarm system."

"I can choose which voice within me that I will listen to and follow."

"I can write a new life script and give up trying to change the past."

"The thoughts that I have and the words that come out of my mouth can be quite persuasive. If I think it or say it, and no one forced me to say it, then I most likely believe it. But, I do not have to believe every thought I have. I do not believe and follow everything that I read in newspapers or hear on TV. I do not have to believe every thought I have."

"My thoughts are hypotheses (hunches) worth testing and not God-given directives."

"I can question and challenge my beliefs and examine the 'If . . . then' and 'Whenever I . . . I will . . . ' rules that I implicitly accept."

"My thoughts and urges are not commandments to act. I have choices."

"If I feel bad and I don't know why, I can use my coping skills."

"If I feel bad and it's made worse by my negative thoughts, I can change my thinking."

"If I feel bad, I can use my direct-action problem-solving coping skills or my emotional - palliative soothing and accepting skills or some combination of these coping skills. I can do whatever the situation calls for."

ACTION #61

I maintain a set of "shatterproof beliefs" or a "moral compass and values" that helps me "move on." I choose to associate with folks who share my positive life-affirming values (See Action #99 for examples of ways to maintain a "moral compass" to guide you).

Useful Information

Trauma has been called the "atom smasher" of one's belief and assumptive world. Trauma can create a rupture in a person's life story. Only through telling new stories are we able to rebuild our sense of self. Through storytelling people begin to comprehend what has happened and begin to understand its significance. By taking control of the stories they tell others and themselves, the way they *re-author* their stories, they can move toward recovery, resilience and personal growth. Transformations arise through the stories they tell.

> *"Human beings are* story tellers. *It is human nature to make meaning of our lives by organizing what happens to us into stories. We live our stories as if they were true. We tell stories to understand what happens to us and to provide us with a framework to shape our new experiences. We are immersed in stories throughout our lives. Our stories help us to construct self-understanding. They help us bind together our thoughts, feelings and behaviors in a way that is continuous with our view of ourselves and our past history"*
>
> —Stephen Joseph, 2011

Quotable Quotes

> *"I now recognize that my memory does not fade. It grows. My memory is malleable and not like a videotape. I have learned that I can manage my memory and thoughts and not have them manage me."*

> *"I want this trauma to lose its gripping quality. I know the memory, the hurt won't go away, but I want to someday become bored with its retelling. I now have a new story to tell—one of survival and purpose."*

> *"I know that the words I use in the stories I tell have power to change my emotions and behavior. My words carry meaning and perspective. My words can inspire and give hope."*

> *"This trauma experience taught me that if this ordeal does not break me, nothing will. After this experience, I fear nothing. Yet, I have also seen how fragile a human being can be, and it made me sensitive to both others' suffering and our own vulnerability."*

ACTION #62

I can use the *language of hope and becoming*. I experience the healing power of storytelling. I can use my "word power" and "change talk." I use as many "Re-verbs" as possible when I share my current personal journey. I can tell others and myself that I am in the process of:

RE-acclimating
RE-activating
RE-assessing
RE-authoring
RE-awaking
RE-balancing
RE-booting
RE-bounding
RE-building
RE-calculating
RE-calibrating
RE-charging
RE-checking
RE-claiming
RE-cognizing
RE-collecting
RE-committing
RE-conceptualizing
RE-conciling
RE-configuring
RE-connecting
RE-considering
RE-construing
RE-constructing
RE-cording
RE-counting
RE-covering
RE-cruiting
RE-cycling
RE-defining
RE-deploying
RE-designing
RE-directing
RE-discovering
RE-doing
RE-drawing
RE-dressing
RE-ducing

RE-engaging
RE-entering
RE-establishing
RE-evaluating
RE-examining
RE-experiencing
RE-fining
Re-fitting
RE-flecting
RE-focusing
RE-framing
RE-fusing
RE-gaining
RE-generating
RE-habilitating
RE-hearsing
RE-integrating
RE-intepreting
RE-inventing
RE-investing
RE-invigorating
RE-joining
RE-kindling
RE-laxing
RE-learning
RE-lieving
RE-linquishing
RE-living
RE-mediating
RE-membering
RE-modeling
RE-moving
RE-negotiating
RE-newing
RE-opening
RE-ordering
RE-organizing
RE-orienting

RE-packing
RE-pairing
RE-peating
RE-placing
RE-plenishing
RE-prioritizing
RE-processing
RE-programming
RE-regulating
RE-scripting
RE-setting
RE-shaping
RE-shuffling
RE-sisting
RE-solving
RE-stabilizing
RE-stating
RE-storing
RE-storying
RE-structuring
RE-suming
RE-taining
RE-telling
RE-thinking
RE-training
RE-transcribing
RE-trieving
RE-uniting
RE-vealing
RE-versing
RE-viewing
RE-vising
RE-visiting
RE-vitalizing
RE-winding
RE-wiring
RE-working
RE-writing

... in order to become more *resilient*.

How To: Use My RE-Verbs

When someone asks me, "How things are going?" or when I want to share how my life is changing, I can choose a RE-verb and answer:

I am glad you asked, because I am in the midst of:

- RE-building my strengths

- RE-charging my batteries

- RE-covering my lost stories and my lost voice

- RE-defining my beliefs

- RE-discovering my strengths

- RE-establishing my relationships

- RE-fusing to allow the trauma to take away my sense of self

- RE-gaining my composure

- RE-gulating my emotions

- RE-interpreting the situation

- RE-learning how to drive more safely

- RE-linquishing my self-defeating and self-destructive life style

- RE-newing my connections with my family and friends

- RE-peating (RE-cycling) what works

- RE-placing my ruminative brooding

- RE-prioritizing my values and goals

- RE-sisting my craving for booze

- RE-sponding flexibly to the demands of a changed world

- RE-storing my sense of competence and RE-claiming personal power

- RE-transcribing (RE-writing) my memories so I no longer have to RE-live and RE-enact them

- RE-working my story so it has a better ending

Now share with the individual *"how"* you are going about doing this. Listen for the number of RE-verbs you include in your conversations.

Quotable Quotes

"By my silence, I allow others to define me. I intend to author my own story."

"I will not allow this event to define me. I intend to move beyond this and write a new chapter. I refuse to view myself as a victim."

"When I tell my story, I have to tell the rest of the story of what I did to survive."

"I have to beware of the stories I tell myself and that I tell others because I can be lived by them."

"I have to watch out for and notice the words I use to tell my story. Words can gain toxicity."

"I can stir up drama and trauma."

"I can increase the number of RE-verbs I use in my stories."

ACTION #63

A common reaction following the experience of traumatic and victimizing experiences is feelings of guilt and shame. Guilt refers to the depreciation of specific actions that are reflected in such "should have" and "could have" statements such as:

- "I should have known better."
- "I should have done something different."
- "I should have prevented it from happening."
- "I should have seen the warning signs earlier."
- "I never should have . . . "

Shame refers to the depreciation or "put down" of self, personality and character.

- "There is something seriously wrong with me."
- "I am evil, a monster."
- "I was totally responsible for what happened. I am inadequate and a bad person."
- "I did not deserve to survive."

Such feelings of guilt and shame and the accompanying self-talk can be debilitating and decrease the quality of life. Thus, the way we think plays an important role in the maintenance and chronicity of posttraumatic stress and adjustment problems. To what degree do you have such emotionally-laden thoughts (What are called "hot cognitions")? Consider the following *Hinge Questions* offered by the psychotherapist Edward Kubany (1994).

- "Do you feel guilty about anything you did/anything you did not do/any feelings you had/any feelings you did not have/any thoughts or beliefs you had?"

- "To what extent do you think you should have known better and could have prevented or avoided the outcomes?"

- "In your judgment, was this outcome foreseeable and preventable?"

- "How could you have known that this was going to happen?"

- "What other options did you have at the time?"

- "Is it possible that you made the best decision under the circumstances and is it possible that choosing other options might have led to worse outcomes?"

Individuals who have lingering guilt and shame hold beliefs of personal responsibility and insufficient justification for their actions. They may feel guilty and ashamed because they judge their actions and inactions as violations of their values that show up as "moral injuries" and "soul wounds."

Guilt and shame are usually a result of *Hindsight Bias*, second-guessing or being a "Monday-morning quarterback." Hindsight bias refers to the tendency to allow current knowledge about event outcomes to bias one's recollections of what one knew *before* the outcomes were known. Hindsight bias contributes to the searching for the answers to "Why" questions for which there are no satisfactory answers. Hindsight bias contributes to "Only . . . if" thinking or what is called contra-factual thinking (the playing and replaying ruminations of alternative actions and outcomes). Individuals now have information that they did not have at the time of the traumatic event. In order to help allay intense feelings of guilt and shame there is a need to help individuals *correct faulty beliefs* that such outcomes were indeed foreseeable and preventable.

> "The bottom line to the successful resolution of guilt is the development of a full recognition of what one knew and believed at the time of the event.
> —Kubany & Ralston, 2008

> "By changing my thinking errors and cognitive distortions, by becoming more aware of my tendency to engage in hindsight bias, I am no longer tormented by guilt."

> I remember my therapist saying: "If I am treating you with respect, and you are treating yourself with disrespect we are cancelling each other out. We need to be working together, on the same side of the ball. And you need to start giving yourself the same respect you want to get and deserve to get from others."

For examples of possible interventions, go to About.com at *ptsd.about.com/od/relatedconditions/a/guilt.htm*

ACTION #64

Ruminate and Brood

Rumination involves *focusing* on one's symptoms and distress and the implications of those symptoms in a repetitive manner (e.g., asking oneself "Why did this happen to me?" "If only this accident had not happened." "If only I had done something different."). Rumination contributes to ongoing threat perception after the experiences of trauma. Ruminations may have a strong *emotional imagery* which can evoke, amplify and prolong intense emotions like anger.

The tendency to ruminate and brood, pine over losses, to not let things go, predicts the persistence of all kinds of emotional distress, depression, Post Traumatic Stress Disorder, anger, anxiety, guilt and shame. Replaying events by continually asking oneself and others "why" questions for which there are no ready or acceptable answers, and engaging in "What if" and "Only if" thinking makes stress worse. Engaging in self-blame, self-condemning and guilt and shame-engendering thoughts and feelings blocks the development of *resilience*. One can be *terrorized* by his or her thoughts.

Such thoughts may come to mind almost automatically and the content is usually unpleasant and negative. Continually asking oneself questions such as "What is it about me that led to these events?" raise self-doubts that can disrupt one's assumptive beliefs about personal safety, predictability of the future, trustworthiness of others and one's sense of forgiveness and justice. Such rumination can increase feelings of nervous tension, negative feelings of sadness, loss and hopelessness. Such feelings can act as internal reminders (retrieval cues) and contribute to the experience of intrusive memories of the traumatic event. As noted, rumination can contribute to the persistence of chronic stress and PTSD.

Instead of engaging in negative forms of rumination, engage in *constructive forms of rumination* and *avoid thinking traps*. Constructive rumination or what has been called the "the work of worrying" pose "How" and "What" questions, for which there are likely potential answers, as compared to problematic rumination and brooding that focus on "Why" questions, for which there are often no satisfying answers. Constructive forms of rumination help individuals make sense of events and develop new ways to look at themselves, the world and the future. Constructive forms of thinking help individuals avoid thinking traps.

Avoid *thinking traps* such as all-or-nothing thinking, engaging in tunnel vision, jumping to conclusions, over-generalizing, impulsive decision-making, being harshly judgmental, getting stuck on "hot spots" or "catastrophizing." Also, holding fears of extremely negative outcomes inevitably occurring, "awfulizing," being perfectionistic, ruminating and brooding, engaging in "only if" hindsight or "Monday-morning quarterbacking" and blaming others. In short, watch out for "Stinking Thinking" and "Thinking Traps" as highlighted by Reivich and Shatte (2002).

The psychologist Albert Ellis said that individuals need to control and avoid telling themselves that "People must/should . . . ," "I must/should . . ." What he called "*must*urbation" or the "Tyranny of shoulds." Ellis warned individuals, "Not to *should* on your head."

Can You Identify the Following "Thinking Traps" in Your Self-Talk?

- Use *polarized thinking* and think in extremes believing that something is either right or wrong, perfect or a complete failure. The use of words like "never," "always," "perfect or horrible," "all or nothing," "black or white," and "dichotomous thinking" will reduce your chances of becoming more resilient.

- Tend to "catastrophize" or "awfulize"—expecting the worst to happen and believe that you will not be able to handle the situation. Jump to the conclusion that you will fail and never be able to cope with the situation. You magnify or exaggerate the negative impact of an event well beyond the facts. Focus your attention on the worse things that can happen. Engaging in the following style of thinking contributes to the persistence of PTSD and accompanying adjustment difficulties.

  - *"These symptoms (intrusive thoughts, flashbacks, lack of concentration and the like) mean I am going mad."*

  - *"Because of this traumatic event, my life is destroyed completely."*

  - *"Bad things always happen to me."*

- Be a *perfectionist* setting very "unrealistic" high standards for yourself and for others and engage in self-criticism or criticism of others for not meeting your standards. Hold unrealistic expectations of yourself and of others. Cling to these old expectations that die hard. Are you too demanding of yourself and of others, too "success-driven", and as a result your own worst enemy?

- Perfectionism is a vulnerability factor for mood swings and negative social interactions. Perfectionism can also interfere with task completion and contribute to rigidity, being over-thorough, repetitive checking, constantly "raising the bar," procrastination and avoidance behaviors and, guilt and anger following failures.

There is nothing wrong in striving for excellence in itself, rather it is when you base your self-worth almost exclusively on striving for standards and concern over mistakes in meeting these standards, when perfectionism becomes a problem that thwarts *resilience*.

How Perfectionistic Are You?

- Do you elevate even minor tasks to being "really important" and get down on yourself if you do not meet your standard?

- What are your reactions to your failure or someone else's failure to meet these standards?

- Are you satisfied after reaching a goal or do you continue to reset your standards higher after meeting a goal?

- Do you avoid or delay trying to meet a goal because of fear of failure?

- Do you tend to discount successes and look for and focus upon failures?

- Do you continually compare your performance with more competent others?

- Do you frequently seek reassurance from others about your performance?

- Are you your own worst critic?

- How can you become less perfectionistic and inoculate yourself to self-doubt and improve your distress tolerance?

What to Do About Your Perfectionism

- Be aware of perfectionism and the impact on yourself and on your relationships.

- Listen for the "shoulds" and "musts" in your self-talk, for they often reveal unrealistic expectations. Learn to spot your unrealistic expectations.

- Loosen rigid rules and lower standards.

- Re-examine and revise your expectations.

- Take small steps toward your goal and feel good about each accomplishment.

- Be more compassionate to self and others.

- Relinquish goals if they are unattainable.

- Stop blaming others for failures and when bad things happen. Avoid immediately assuming that it is someone else's fault and react automatically.

- Consider alternative explanations, instead of automatically feeling as if you are being mistreated and thinking, "It's not fair."

- Create a pie chart and determine how much of the task performance outcome is due to your efforts and then figure out what other factors may have come into play.

- Keep things in perspective.

- See references on ways to reduce perfectionism such as Antony and Swinson (1998).

Here are other examples of ways to undermine your *resilience:*

Feel Helpless—Lack of control or influence about events that happen in your life ("I love your ideas; I'm just too stressed out to use them.")

Feel Hopeless—Nothing will ever change, nor improve.

Feel Like a Burden—People would be better off if I weren't around anymore.

Feel Isolated and Alienated—Others don't understand and can't help me. I feel unloved and unappreciated.

> *"Nobody is there for me."*

> *"Her asking me if I need help must mean she does not think I can cope and handle this on my own."*

> *"I am a marked person and I will never be the same."*

Feel Resentment—which is a form of chronic deep-seated anger that re-emerges and continues long after a provocation or personal injury. You can whip up and inflame your anger and resentment. Anger has been characterized as a flame and resentment like a hot coal that simmers. Holding onto resentment, "not letting it go," can have deleterious health effects and undermine the development of resilience and well-being. Resentment can feed on itself, like an untreated wound that spreads like an infection.

Individuals who are persistently resentful have higher blood pressure, higher rates of heart disease, lower immune functioning, more depression, higher rates of marital discord and divorce.

Hold a Confirmatory Bias—Engage in "Seek and ye shall find" thinking. Search for and interpret information in ways that confirm what you already believe. Only attend to and accept information that is consistent with your prior beliefs. Like a "self-fulfilling" prophecy, making negative predictions about the future, may lead to self-defeating actions.

Engage in Self-Handicapping Behaviors—A ploy by which individuals deliberately use excuse-generating acts where they expect to do poorly or fail. For example, fail to rehearse before an audition to create an acceptable excuse.

In Contrast

There is a need to adopt a resilient mindset.

In contrast to the negative behaviors listed above, there is a need to *put resentment to rest*. Like a playwright who rewrites and edits a script, there is a need for the resentful individual to craft new self-talk and learn to produce a new "inner dialogue." There is a need to replace counter-productive self-talk with productive self-talk. Some individuals have found it helpful to engage in a symbolic act such as writing a letter to the person(s) for whom they feel resentment (but not sending it) and then burning it, or confronting the other person(s) in their imagination. In some instances, resentful individuals may require the help of a professional counsellor or chaplain to put their old anger and resentment to rest.

Instead of creating roadblocks of a negative script which are counterproductive and self-defeating, I can adopt a resilient mindset.

> *As described by two psychologists, Robert Brooks and Sam Goldstein (2003), "a* resilient mindset *is composed of several main features. These include feeling in control of one's life, knowing how to fortify one's 'stress hardiness,' being empathic, displaying effective communication, and other interpersonal skills, possessing problem-solving and decision-making skills, establishing realistic goals and expectations, learning from both success and failure, being a compassionate and contributing member of society. Possessing a* resilient mindset *does not imply that one is free from stress, pressure, negative feelings, conflict, but rather that one can successfully cope with problems as they arise. Accepting change and suffering as part of living"* (Brooks & Goldstein, 2003).

An excellent example of a *resilient mindset* was offered by Terry Waite (1995), who was captured and held hostage in solitary confinement by Islamic Jihad terrorists for four years in Beirut, Lebanon. After being chained, beaten, and subjected to mock executions, he said, upon his release:

> *"I said three things on release: no regret, no self-pity and no sentimentality. I tried to turn the experience around. Suffering is universal; you attempt to subvert it, so that it does not have a destructive, negative effect. You turn it around so that it becomes a creative, positive force."*

ACTION #65

Instead of having "whine time" I can "garden my mind" by thinking about something that brings me joy; remember something that I find fascinating, humorous or positive that I want to accomplish. I can look for opportunities for self-discovery. I can use the words "challenges in my life" instead of the words "stressors in my life." I can nurture a positive view of myself, others and the future.

I have to be careful not to *over generalize.*

- "Having been helpless does not mean that one is a helpless person."

- "Having been violated does not mean that one has to live one's life in constant readiness for its re-enactment."

- "Having been treated as disposable does not mean that one is worthless."

- "Taking the painful risk of bearing witness does not mean that the world will listen, learn, change and become a better place."

- "Having witnessed or experienced evil does not mean that betrayal is an overriding human behavior."

- "Hurting does not mean that I am broken."

Useful Information

When I tell my "story" to myself and to others, I need to include the following "change talk" verbs and expressions. I can now:

Absorb	Broaden	Dampen
Accept	Build	Decipher
Accommodate	Catch	Decompress
Acknowledge	Change	Decouple
Adapt	Check	Deescalate
Allay	Choose	Defuse
Anticipate	Clarify	Demonstrate
Appreciate	Compartmentalize	Deregulate
Ask	Confront	Develop
Assimilate	Connect	Disconfirm
Awaken	Control	Discover
Balance	Counteract	Discuss
Belong	Craft	Disengage
Bolster	Create	Dismantle
Bounce Back	Cultivate	Distinguish

Down-regulate	Improvise	Promote
Edit	Incorporate	Propel
Embark	Increase	Push Through
Embrace	Inoculate	Question
Empower	Integrate	Savor
Enable	Instill	Seek
Endure	Interrupt	Self-generate
Engender	Invite	Self-soothe
Engage	Journey	Sense of Humor
Enhance	Label	Share
Envision	Maintain	Shift
Equip	Make Meaning	Solidify
Expand	Make Peace	Springboard
Explore	Manage	Stabilize
Extend	Manipulate	Strengthen
Facilitate	Master	Stretch
Fend Off	Mobilize	Strive
Figure Out	Modulate	Subdue
Find	Monitor	Surprise Myself
Fine-tune	Move Towards	Sustain
Finesse	Neutralize	Thrive
Be Flexible	Notice	Tolerate
Focus	Nudge	Transcend
Forestall	Observe	Transform
Fortify	Open	Trigger
Foster	Overcome	Troubleshoot
Fuel	Override	Try Out
Generate	Pinpoint	Tune Into
Grasp	Plan	Uncover
Grow	Potentiate	Unleash
Harmonize	Praise	Unwind
Harness	Prepare	Uplift
Hope	Prevail	Use
Identify	Prevent	Work Through
Implement	Preview	

(Also remember to use all of your RE-verbs—Action #62).

Can you give examples of how you can now "Notice, Catch, Interrupt, Plan, Question, Fine-tune, Share, Test-out, Try"? How are you going about "Expanding your coping tool kit"; "Exploring new options"; "Using your sense of humor"? These are action verbs that can move you toward *resilience* and *personal growth*.

For example, I can now:

- "Accept the ways things turn out."

- "Ask for help."

- "Focus on my strengths and what I did to survive."

- "Identify what is really important in my life."

- "Implement new strategies."

- "Increase my capacity to manage my emotions."

- "Integrate my traumatic experiences."

- "Invite optimism into my life."

- "Override my stress-alarm system."

- "Self-soothe my emotions."

- "Share my story of survival and strengths."

ACTION #66

I can create a "healing story." Resilient individuals have a particular way of creating a personal narrative that they share with others and that they tell themselves. The ways I tell my story will be central to whether I develop Posttraumatic Growth or Posttraumatic Stress Disorder and related adjustment problems. In what ways do I tell my stories?

How To: Create a Healing Story

One of the things that differentiate us from animals is the fact that we can listen to other people's stories and they in turn can listen to ours. We can even tell ourselves stories. Instead of calling our species Homo Sapiens, we would be better characterized as "Homo Narrans"- - the story-telling species.

Every year of our lives, we add well over half a million minutes to our banks of experience. How we organize, chronicle, interpret, imbue them with meaning, share these experiences and weave them together into "stories" will influence how *resilient* we become.

We don't just tell stories, stories tell us. The tales we tell hold powerful sway over our memories, behaviors and even identities. Stories are fundamental to our being. Once you tell a story, it is hard to get out of that story's framework. Over time, the stories we tell tend to get more dramatic. The stories we tell others and to ourselves grip our imagination, impregnate our hearts and animate our spirit.

As human beings we are story tellers, but beware of the stories you tell, you will have to live by them.

There is a "metamorphosis of speech." The stories that we hear from others turn into conscious inner speech, and then they in turn, become implicit, automatic, unconscious scripts and beliefs that guide and influence our behaviors. Like a pupa that turns into a caterpillar that turns into a butterfly that gives flight, the stories we tell ourselves and others have also been transformed.

- Following exposure to traumatic events, up to 30% of individuals may evidence chronic distress, and even develop Post-traumatic Stress Disorder and related adjustment problems. Research by Ehlers and Clark (2000) indicated that individuals with PTSD have memory accounts that are usually brief, skeletal, fact-oriented, and journalistic without emotional depth. Their memories are often fragmented, insufficiently elaborated; details may be missing, lacking coherence of a beginning, middle and end, made up of bits and pieces. Their memories are also over-generalized (lacking in detail) that intensify their sense of helplessness and hopelessness and impairs their problem-solving abilities. Their traumatic narrative is *inadequately integrated* into their autobiographical memories. Their stories have an inflated sense of responsibility with accompanying excessive guilt and shame. They misperceive their distressing reactions as signs that they are "going crazy" and that they are "worthless" and that they are a burden on others. Their stories convey the belief that the world is unsafe and unpredictable, unjust, and that people are unappreciative of their sacrifices, untrustworthy and unsympathetic. They may feel marginalized, isolated, alienated and rejected.

  For those who continue to struggle with the aftermath of the experience of traumatic and victimizing events, their trauma-related memories are viewed as being unwanted, uninvited and involuntary, poorly controlled, nor accepted. The trauma memories are mainly cue-driven so that any stimuli that resemble those that occurred surrounding the traumatic events can trigger re-experiencing symptoms and accompanying distressing feelings. The individual may act as if the threat is still present and re-experience it as if it was happening right now, rather than being a memory from the past. Such intrusive thoughts and accompanying intense feelings have been characterized like an "unwanted roommate" who keeps showing up but any attempt to get rid of him or her comes to no avail. The more one tries, the more bothersome the roommate becomes. But, the more one tries to avoid and stop him/her, the more persistent he/she becomes.

  In their attempt to stop or suppress such thoughts and feelings, and in their efforts to avoid reminders, they may paradoxically experience even more intrusive distressing thoughts, images and intense feelings and urges. Their coping efforts at suppressing actually *backfire* and act like a boomerang, as noted by Wegner (1994). They may try to cope by self-medicating (using alcohol, drugs), by trying distractions of engaging in high-risk reckless behaviors (withdrawing, isolating themselves, being hyper vigilant, on "sentry duty" all the time) and by engaging in "safety behaviors"—constantly checking and rechecking and engaging in avoidant behaviors. But, such avoidant thinking and behaviors about the traumatic events prevents individuals from processing and incorporating such events into their life stories. It precludes them from obtaining corrective information that may help change any mistaken beliefs they may hold. Such avoidant behaviors prevent them from rebuilding their basic beliefs about themselves, the world and the future. In short, inadvertently, unwittingly, and perhaps, even unknowingly they make their level of distress even worse. Research indicates that the more individuals attempt to tamp down such unwanted thoughts, or when they try intentionally not to think of something, it has the opposite effect. One part of our mind does avoid the forbidden thought, but another part "checks in" every so often to make sure the thought is not coming up—therefore ironically bringing it to mind.

- In contrast, *resilient* individuals are psychologically agile and flexible in how they tell their stories. They view the traumatic events as being time-limited experiences that do not necessarily have negative implications for the future. They view their reactions such as intrusive recollections, sleep disturbance, nightmares, difficulties concentrating and the like as a normal part of recovery that follows from upsetting events. When *resilient* individuals tell their stories they include examples of what they did and how they coped and survived. They tell the "rest of their story." They weave into their story-telling the upside of what happened, as well. They view any traumatic events that they experienced as a "turning point," a "fork in the road," a "temporary detour" on their personal life journey. Their stories are rich with healing metaphors, mottos, and examples of pain, but also survival. The metaphors that individuals use serve as a guide to their actions. Consider the differences and impact of individuals calling themselves "victims," or "prisoners of the past," or "walking time bombs," "emotional zombies," as compared to "survivors," or "thrivers." What metaphors do you incorporate in your story-telling?

- Even though it is emotionally painful, *resilient* individuals are able to process their trauma-related memories, rather than avoid them. They are able to metaphorically "pack away" their memories as if they were "emotional luggage" or "file" them away as in a filing cabinet or cupboard. Resilient individuals can learn to choose when they open and close the valise, filing cabinet or cupboard. They are able to develop voluntary and deliberate control over their memories, as they repack and reorder their "emotional luggage." By incorporating these trauma memories as part of their reconfigured and reauthored stories, they are able to place what happened in a broader autobiographical context. Not sharing such accounts, "clamming up," only makes things worse.

Resilient individuals feel more in charge of how they tell and share their traumatic material. They can choose when, where and how they share their experiences. They tell their "stories." Their stories do not tell them.

Stories are the means by which coping processes exert their influence. Retelling stories to supportive others allows individuals to generate "new stories" about who they are, what role trauma played in their lives and how these events fit into their future plans.

Story telling permits one to look at past events through a different set of lenses and helps develop a new outlook so the trauma memories will come to elicit less distress, fear, sadness, guilt, shame, and anger. Remember, it is not that one experiences such feelings, but what one does with these emotions that determines the level of recovery, resilience and personal growth.

- Resilient individuals may take some time to experience grief or unhappiness, distress, anger and loss, sadness and anxiety, guilt and shame which improve their abilities to better appreciate the world in all of its complexity and richness.

- Resilient individuals tend to tell stories that have "redemptive sequences" in which bad events have good outcomes, as compared to "contamination sequences" when the reverse happens.

- Resilient individuals *slow down* how they tell their stories and break their experiences into pieces. They examine the pieces in terms of all the complexities and then they connect the dots. They do not act like a "Monday morning quarterback," who has hindsight bias, blaming themselves for things they did not know at the time.

- Resilient individuals are on the lookout for unexplored "open spaces" in their narrative that act as a *guide* to new goals and alternatives. Redemption stories bolster hope; strengthen self-confidence that their efforts will bear fruit. They strengthen the belief in the possibility of positive outcomes. Changes in story-telling provide access to new solutions.

- Resilient individuals tend to tell *coherent stories* that create meaning out of their stressful life experiences and in which they see themselves as "personal agents" often with the assistance of others, of the positive changes that they have been able to bring about. These *coherent narratives* are clearly articulated, detailed, logical and well organized. Such coherent stories are salutary and help reduce distress. They increase the survivor's sense of control over his or her experiences, reduce feelings of chaos and increase the sense that the world is predictable, orderly and beneficent. Coherent story-telling can provide a degree of "closure" by helping make sense of what happened and how people responded. Narrative coherence conveys feelings of personal self-efficacy and points a direction to the future. It is not enough to help individuals create a trauma narrative, but it is also essential to help individuals integrate such thoughts and feelings into a consistent coherent meaningful experience and story. Trauma is only one part of an individual's life, rather than the defining aspect.

- Resilient individuals have the ability and penchant to tell their fragmented stories in a chronological narrative with before, middle and post-trauma exposure or post-deployment parts. They are able to *integrate* what happened during deployment into their autobiographical memory and let the "past be the past." As one resilient individual stated: "I have no interest in going back to the past and getting stuck again." Resilient individuals refuse to allow the "trauma stories and images" to become dominant in their narrative and take away their sense of identity. They can disentangle themselves from the influence and lingering impact of traumatic events. They engage in a narrative healing process.

- Resilient individuals avoid "thinking traps" that can derail their story-telling (See Action #64). Instead, they incorporate in their story-telling "cherished recollections," "fond memories," a "heritage of remembrances," "change talk" (See Action #65), "RE-verbs" (See Action #62). Resilient individuals tell stories that enrich their lives and help them get past their personal challenges. They tell stories that they can pass onto the next generation, as "lessons learned."

- Resilient individuals tell their stories first and then they live their way into them. They may act "as if" they are characters in the stories that they tell. There may be a certain amount of "fake it, until you make it."

- Resilient individuals are "thought detectives", noticing when they are falling into "thinking traps" and engaging in "negative self-talk." They have the ability and motivation to ask themselves a series of *Hinge Questions*.

  - "Can I break my negative self-talk habits?"

  - "Can I notice, interrupt the chain of negative self-talk?"

  - "Am I blowing things out of proportion?"

  - "Am I using self-talk that is extreme or exaggerated with words like always, never, every time, should, must?"

  - "Does this *always* happen?"

  - "Do I *never* get a chance to do what I want?"

  - "Am I thinking in all-or-none terms?"

  - "Do I think mainly about bad things that happened and not about the good things?"

  - "What is the evidence for or against my beliefs?"

- "Can I put things in perspective?"

- "Can I control my what-if thinking patterns and limit rumination?"

- "What is the worst thing that can happen if it comes true?"

- "And if it does occur what would be so terrible?"

- "Then what would happen?"

- "What would that mean?"

- "How likely is that to happen?"

- "Can I handle the situation if that happens?"

- "Can I change to a more balanced self-talk, instead of magnifying the negatives and minimizing the positives?"

- "Can I restate my negative self-talk so it is in a form that helps me achieve my goals of . . . ?"

- Resilient individuals listen to the stories they tell others and that they tell themselves. Their stories include:

  - Ways of facing, deliberately retrieving, voluntarily processing and sharing emotionally-charged trauma-related memories in an organized, controlled and coherent fashion

  - Consciously incorporating helpful and "wise" metaphors of survival and growth, as compared to negatively-loaded "victim" metaphors

  - Redemptive (positive endings) sequences that include what they did to survive

  - RE-words and change talk action verbs

  - Goal statements and "how to" pathways thinking

  - Problem-solving strategies, Action Plans with "if . . . then" statements and expressions of self-confidence and "grit" (dogged persistence)

  - Expressions of optimism, including statements of benefit finding and benefit remembering ("Silver lining" thinking), downward comparisons ("Could have been worse") statements

- Meaning-making statements ("Making a gift," "Sharing lessons learned" statements)

- Adoption of *resilience* and *growth mindset* where change is possible.

Ask yourself and others, if the stories you tell are elaborate, organized, coherent (having a beginning, middle and end) that are now integrated as part of your autobiographical memory? Does your story open up new possibilities for change and provide a positive blueprint for the future? If not, how can you begin to change your story? What can you do to develop a *resilient mindset?*

ACTION #67

Here are other examples of ways to improve my *thinking processes, self-talk* and *cognitive fitness.* (Please email these suggestions to *examples@roadmaptoresilience.org*)

_____

_____

_____

_____

Behavioral Fitness

"The key to successful coping is flexibility of matching the coping strategies to the demands of the situation and to one's goals."

"Resilience skills are like a muscle in a body that needs exercise, practice and usage in order to develop and to be replenished"

"Resilient individuals are masters of innovation. Instead of following a prescribed automatic habitual behavioral script, resilient individuals are able to alter, regulate, override, break free and choose from a variety of coping options."

"Individuals who have better self-control and will power (delay of gratification, show GRIT, are strategic) do better interpersonally, suffer less after experiencing stressors, are better adjusted and perform better at school and on the job."

"Resilient individuals monitor, modify and evaluate their emotional reactions to accomplish a goal. They manage taxing circumstances, reduce or tolerate stress and conflict and accept what is beyond their control or cannot be changed."

Behavioral fitness is the ability to form and implement Behavioral Action Plans; to be flexible and adaptable in the face of change and to make maximal use of abilities and resources.

Behavioral Fitness is reflected in the willingness to try out new strategies and learn from mistakes and setbacks. Behaviorally fit individuals see themselves as organized, industrious, conscientious, committed and self-controlled, all of which contributes to their *resilience*.

ACTION #68

I restore or develop "safe routines" that work for me and that allow me to decompress, de-stress when necessary. I can establish a "regular routine," use time management strategies, prioritize, "de-clutter" my mind, structure my time constructively and fill my days with health-promoting activities. I can take R-and-R time and engage in enjoyable relaxing activities. I give myself a "stress break" and schedule time for myself. I can schedule intimate time with others. I make sure I keep pleasurable things in my life, and try to maintain my routines, as much as possible.

But, following a set of daily routines does *not* preclude being *open to new experiences.* Individuals who cope more effectively with role transitions tend to be more *creative;* they prefer novelty, new experiences, and have wide interests. They also have confidence in their ability to succeed and they have a firm sense of self as being "creative." In contrast, less creative individuals are more attracted to certainty and lack confidence in their ability to achieve in novel tasks. Creative individuals seek out novelty in their everyday lives and take on new challenges.

Quotable Quotes

"While I like my daily routines, I am always on the look out for those situations that challenge and will surprise me."

"I can stay organized by creating a daily schedule of tasks and activities."

"I was always very much the caretaker, taking care of other people's needs and I am beginning to realize you know that I deserve the same level of care and support that I was giving to others."

"I found out that when I was tending my garden, I was actually tending myself."

ACTION #69

I stay calm even under pressure. I can think before I act out and not be impulsive, keep my cool and use my positive coping self-statements. I can use a variety of additional relaxation procedures including working out, breathing and safe imagery exercises, mindfulness skills, letting go in a non- judgmental fashion, meditation, yoga, doing pleasurable things, distraction procedures and taking a "time out." I find healthy and safe ways to blow off steam.

Useful Information

The relaxation response is the body's innate antidote to the stress response. One cannot be both stressed out and relaxed at the same time. Relaxation is a skill, like any other skill, and requires deliberate practice. Not just any kind of practice, but consistent effort (See Action #41 and #9).

Quotable Quotes

"I learned that anger can be a stand in emotion for fear, or feeling hurt, humiliated, abandoned. Anger can be a signal that tells me something else is bothering me."

"I learned to be an emotional detective and not act out."

"I learned I had to calm myself down and take a 'time out' and regulate down my emotional arousal and just listen to what my wife was saying about the events in her day. I have learned to edit what I say."

"I learned how to control my self-talk and use 'positive coping self-statements' before, during and after stressful situations."

How To: Use Positive Coping Self-Statements

Following are some sample self-statements you can say to yourself in place of negative "automatic thoughts" that may occur in stressful situations. Try them out.

Before—in preparation of stressful situations:

- "What is my game plan and what is my back-up plan?"
- "I have handled situations like this in the past."
- "I have a lot of coping skills I can use."
- "I can talk to others who have dealt with such stressful situations, beforehand."
- "Other positive self-statements I can use *before* are:

  _____

  _____

  _____

During the course of stressful situations:

- "I can manage this situation, if I take it one step at a time."
- "I can notice if I am getting uptight and catch myself."
- "I can view this situation as a *challenge* and as an *opportunity* to improve, rather than as a personal threat."
- "Just use my tactical breathing skills and lower my heart rate by 6 to 10 beats per minute. Take a slow deep breath."
- "I do not have to work myself up."
- "Relax. Calm down. I am in control."
- "Keep focused on the present. What do I have to do?"
- "I have gotten through tougher situations than this before. This will *not* overwhelm me. It just feels that way sometimes."
- "These feelings are a signal to use my coping skills."
- "Other positive self-statements I can use *during* are:

  _____

  _____

  _____

After the stressful situation is over:

- "I have to figure out how things went. What worked? What did not work? Debrief myself."
- "I need to pat myself on the back and give myself credit for making a good effort and for any improvement, large or small."
- "I am learning how to deal with these situations more effectively. Next time I can do even better."
- "It did not go as bad as I expected."
- "I am making progress."
- "I handled it pretty well. Wait until I share this with others."
- "Other positive self-statements I can use *after* are:

_____

_____

ACTION #70

I plan ahead and prepare myself for possible high-risk situations. Figure out what to expect and create a game plan and a back-up plan. Learn what to watch out for and know when to leave and when to return. In order to bolster my self-confidence in doing these things, I will answer *honestly* the following *Hinge Questions*:

Taking Stock or a Personal Inventory

- What do I see as my own personal strengths or abilities?

- What things about myself am I most proud?

- What do other people say are my positive qualities?

- What do they say are the positive qualities of my friends and family members?

- How have I used my personal strengths and abilities to achieve goals or deal with challenges in the past?

- How do I think I could use my strengths to help me achieve my current goals?

- What skills do I already possess that I think can be transferred to the present situation?

- What kind of new skills do I need, and how can I acquire them?

- What contacts do I have that might help?

- Finally, what would it be like if I did not have this problem any more?

How To: Begin to Plan Your Next Steps

Begin by choosing some "personal challenge" you wish to work on. Does it have to do with re-integration issues (family-related, work-related, health-related, and stress-related)? Now on a scale from one to ten, where rating from one being the worst possible solution to a rating of ten being the best possible solution, where would you rate your confidence that you can achieve this goal?

- What challenge did you select?

- What rating of Self-confidence did you offer?

- What led you to offer a rating that was not a "one," if you did not choose a "one" rating?

- What are things that give you hope that things can change for the better?

- How do you think you will be able to work on your goal of...?

- What else can you try?

- What might get in the way of doing...?

- You would have to be strong (creative, clever, resourceful) to find a way around that. I wonder, how you would do it?

- What exactly are you committing yourself to doing?

- What will the best future look like for you?

- What will happen? Who will be there with you?

- What will it take to make this a reality?

ACTION #71

I can break my goals and tasks into subtasks with sub-goals. I can set specific, concrete, attainable subgoals. I can identify the "when, where and how" of each action that will occur, and thus, reduce procrastination and hasten the initiation and execution of the behavior. Research by Ehlers and Clark indicates that when individuals are depressed or experience Post traumatic stress reactions, they tend to set "abstract" level goals and make limited progress. Chunk the situation into doable subtasks so I do not get overwhelmed. (See Action #47 for a discussion of "S.M.A.R.T." Goals).

Useful Information

Self-efficacy and self-confidence are cultivated by taking small steps. Find the right challenge, not too challenging, and not too simple. Create an image of yourself as a capable person of meeting and overcoming challenges. Remember that every journey begins with a single step.

Think of a time in the past when you set yourself a goal and achieved it. Ask yourself the following *Hinge Questions*:

- "How did I get motivated?"

- "How did I keep my motivation going?"

- "What were the strategies I used to accomplish this goal?"

- "How did I know I was making progress?"

- "Who did I call upon to help me work on this goal?"

- "Have I ever helped someone else work to achieve his/her goal? What did I do to help? Can I use these strategies on myself?"

Quotable Quotes

"I can celebrate my small behavioral triumphs that I make everyday because my success, no matter how small, inspire me and helps me feel good about myself."

"I can confront my feelings of ambivalence about changing and gently move toward action by considering the pros and cons of various actions, including sometimes doing nothing."

"I can adopt a 'growth mindset' of change by working at achieving my goals versus a 'fixed mindset' that I do not have the capacity or ability to improve things or succeed."

"I just let time go by and its not as stressful to me. I do not know if this makes sense, but then I can tackle one thing at a time."

"I have a strong desire to avoid repeating the mistakes my parents made."

ACTION #72

I *avoid avoidance*, since avoidance of my problems and the triggers and reminders slows the recovery process and is likely to make things worse. I can learn to tolerate, face, confront and re-experience what I encountered without falling apart. I "fast-forward" to the *present*, look to the future and get unstuck from the past. I can make peace with the past.

Avoidance behavior maintains anxiety disorders such as PTSD. Such avoidance behaviors may include "situational avoidance" of places, people and other reminders like sounds, smells, and sights (movies, television programs, and books) that remind the individual of the traumatic events, and "cognitive avoidance" of bothersome thoughts and conversational topics.

As highlighted before, there is a paradoxical (or opposite) effect when individuals attempt to deliberately and actively monitor and suppress unwanted mental states in order to control them. Such avoidant and suppressing efforts tend to actually cause them to occur. Avoidance efforts have a "boomerang" opposite effect. Avoidance forms of coping play a role in the generation of stress, contributing to a higher number of daily hassles and stressful life events which are linked to depressive symptoms. Avoidant behaviors have the negative effect of reducing access to social supports and the opportunity to benefit from the therapeutic effects of talking about emotions with others.

Useful Information

Avoidance can be a helpful protection in the short-term as a way of pacing or dosing oneself and gradually overcoming fear and demonstrating courage. But, when avoidance behaviors become habitual and prolonged, they can become problematic and psychologically destructive. Avoidance can lead to problems piling up. Avoidance behaviors prevent people from working through their emotions and limit their lives as they become hyper vigilant to possible reminders and triggers. Prolonged avoidance can become a negative downward spiral.

As the adage goes:

> *"It helps to get back on the horse after one has been thrown."*

Gradual exposure and reexperience is the most effective way for the body's "fear alert system" to be deactivated and for the mind's "alarm system" to be switched off.

Quotable Quotes

> *"I have learned to loosen my grip on destructive emotions. I can steer myself in the right direction, with courage. It wasn't easy."*

"When I realized I wasn't the only one with these problems and who felt like this, it made all the difference."

"I finally realized that avoiding my problems was not going to solve them."

"I thought I would fall apart if I had to reexperience and resolve my traumatic events. I learned that I did not need protection from that which I had previously worked so hard to avoid."

"I learned to tolerate and accept discomfort that comes when the reminders of the past come and I can neutralize and transform these events."

"I learned to make it palatable and gave up the fight with the past."

"I learned to consider in detail the material I would otherwise avoid. I had to learn to sustain my attention in areas that are difficult and challenging."

"I had to learn to put these traumatic memories in the midst of my life story. It is only part of my memory, not my whole memory."

"If the river turns, and you do not turn, you end up on dry land."

"I have learned to shake off threats that do not materialize."

ACTION #73

I improve my "people-picking" ability and avoid people and situations that set me off, get me into trouble and contribute to my relapse.

Quotable Quotes

"If bad relationships messed me up, then it follows that I need good relationships to help me heal."

"I am more willing to remove myself from a bad relationship, than I used to be. I can take a break or end them. I am more comfortable with the idea of being alone. I'm learning to accept the fact that what one person wants does not determine what happens in a relationship. It is a two way street."

"I am learning to set boundaries with people, so I have to learn how to say "No." I can now say I can't do this or I can't do that. I am getting better at it."

"I am powerless over everyone, but myself. What they say, do, think and feel is their right as long as it doesn't hurt others. It is not my job to be a parent, teacher, police officer, spiritual leader or critic that takes time and robs me of energy. I can

focus on problem-solving how I decide to react to what they do or just accept what I cannot change. Either way, I can be calm. Either way, they will continue to do what they choose to do."

—Robert Nay, *Taking Charge of Your Anger*

ACTION #74

I take a "news holiday" or time out from news accounts or other information sources that upset me (TV, internet, newspapers).

ACTION #75

I learn to co-exist with my difficult memories and *not* allow my emotions to "hijack" my actions and cripple me.

Quotable Quotes

"This traumatic event was a turning point in my life. But how I tell my story to myself and to others can trap me in the past."

"Life shapes us. No, that is not quite right. It is more accurate to say, "What we do with what life throws at us shapes us."

"If you have skeletons in your closet, you had best teach them how to dance."

ACTION #76

I know when and how to self-disclose and share my story, and what I have learned with trusted others. This is a "give–back" activity and I can make sure I include the "whole or rest of the story" of what I did to survive and thrive.

Quotable Quotes

"I am at a 'narrative fork in the road' and I can choose which stories I tell others and which stories I tell myself."

"I can revise, reframe, reinterpret and edit my story."

"I have to remember to include the rest of the story of survival."

"The stories I tell determine how I see myself (my self-view)."

ACTION #77

I join a social group or organization that gives my life purpose and helps me find meaning. I can benefit from their story-telling and find role models to emulate. I will participate in the social activity even though I may not feel like it at first. Social isolation and avoidance only make things worse. Social support increases my well-being and limits distress. Being connected makes it easier to obtain coping information, get practical help and gives me a sense of being understood and accepted. Being part of a group provides a sense of connectedness and collective efficacy to work together toward a specific goal.

ACTION #78

I ease into new roles at home, at work and in leisure activities. I need to read the scene, collect information and see how things have changed. I need to renegotiate my role and responsibilities.

ACTION #79

I adopt a "can-do" attitude of doing "whatever it takes." I can experiment with new behaviors and new ways of doing things; pick a tool from my "resilience toolkit" and practice it. I can *cultivate my will power.* Will power is not just a matter of having it or not. Not only can I make changes, but I can keep it up.

"The willingness to do creates the ability to do."

Useful Information

"For resilient individuals, readjustment is a marathon, not a sprint. It is a team sport, like a relay race. They have the will/stamina to make the transition successfully. Readjustment to civilian life takes time. Readjustment is a process, a journey, not an event, and is something everyone is involved in."

As noted in Action #28, resilient service members have grit, will and stamina to make the transition to civilian life successfully. They are determined to be a member of the 70% who "make it."

"Resilient individuals have confidence in their ability to make a smooth transition and handle bumps and detours on their journey."

The trauma expert Stephen Joseph (2011) has summarized this "can-do" attitude in the form of a "T.H.R.I.V.E." model. "T.H.R.I.V.E." is an acronym that reminds individuals of the steps required to bolster their resilience and journey toward personal growth.

T.H.R.I.V.E. Model:

T - **Take Stock**
H - **Harvest Hope**
R - **Re-author** one's "story"
I - **Identify Change**
V - **Value Change**
E - **Express Change in Action**

How can you "take stock?" Think of times when you felt a little better and when things were going your way. What happened? What were you doing or *not* doing; feeling or *not* feeling; thinking or *not* thinking? How were others reacting to you when these better times occurred? Once you figure out what works, *do more of it.*

ACTION #80

I find comfort in reading books, the Bible, watching movies of inspiring accounts of resilient individuals. (See the HBO movie *Alive Day Memories, Home from Iraq* with James Gandolfini—alias Tony Soprano. Go to *www.TED.com* and search for the video of Jill Bolte Taylor story of how she recovered from a stroke).

Here are examples of books of personal growth and resilience where individuals had to overcome adversities.

- Maya Angelou, *I Know Why the Caged Bird Sings*

- Lance Armstrong, *It's Not About the Bike: My Journey Back to Life*

- Thomas Buergenthal, *A Lucky Child: A Memoir of Surviving Auschwitz As a Young Boy*

- Romeo Dallaire, *Shake Hands With the Devil*

- Joan Didion, *The Year of Magical Thinking*

- Michael J. Fox, *Always Looking Up*

- Viktor Frankl, *Man's Search for Meaning*

- Edward M. Kennedy, *True Compass: A Memoir*

- June Cerza Kolf, *When Will I Stop Hurting? Dealing With a Recent Death*

- Nelson Mandela, *Long Walk to Freedom*

- Brook Noel, *I Wasn't Ready to Say Goodbye: Surviving, Coping and Healing After the Sudden Death of a Loved One*

- Christopher Reeve, *Still Me*

- Elyn Saks, *The Center Cannot Hold*

- Nancy Sherman, *The Untold War*

- J.B. Taylor, *My Stroke of Insight*

- Terry Waite, *Taken On Trust*

Useful Information

It is reported that the celebrated warrior Alexander the Great, who was tutored by the philosopher Aristotle, slept with a copy of Homer's *The Illiad*, personally annotated by Aristotle, under his pillow because of its military virtue, knowledge and evidence of resilience.

ACTION #81

I can gather information about how my family and I can cope more effectively, about military benefits and employment opportunities. *The good news is that I am not alone.* I can gather information, access assistance and mobilize resources. There are many websites, organizations and programs currently available that provide valuable information and countless services and benefits to service members and their families. For example, there are resources and rehabilitation services that provide patient and family education, training in self-care and independent living skills, social skills training, supported housing and employment, peer counselling and vet-to-vet services, Internet-based self-help rehabilitation and intensive case management.

Here is a sample of these resources for veterans and their family members:

U.S. Dept. of Veteran's Affairs (Mobile App)
  http://www.ptsd.va.gov/public/pages/ptsdcoach.asp

Military One Source
  1-800-242-9647
  www.militaryonesource.com

Joint Services Support
  www.jointservicessupport.org

Making Connections
www.MakeTheConnection.net/stories-of-connection

Military Homefront
www.militaryhomefront.dod.mil/

Center for Deployment Psychology
www.deploymentpsych.org

Combat Stress Intervention Program
www.copingaftercombat.com

Real Warriors
www.realwarriors.net

After Deployment
www.afterdeployment.org

Federal Recovery Coordination Program
www.oefoif.va.gov

Comprehensive Soldier Fitness
www.army.mil/csf
https://www.resilience.army.mil/

Defense Center of Excellence
www.dcoe.health.mil/default.aspx

Center for Women Veterans
www1.va.gov/womenvet

Hearts Toward Home International
www.heartstowardhome.com

National Center for PTSD
www.ncptsd.va.gov

Tricare Health Care Programs
www.tricare.mil

National Center for Telehealth and Technology
www.t2health.org

Defense and Veterans' Brain Injury Center
dvbic.org

Disabled American Veterans
www.dav.org

Veterans' Treatment Court
   www.buffaloveteranscourt.org
   www.nadcp.org/vets

Employment information websites for veterans:
   www.Recruitmilitary.com
   store.samhsa.gov/home
   www.esgr.org
   www.dol.gov/vets/programs/main.htm
   www.VetJobs.com
   www.MilitaryHire.com
   www.Military.com
   www.rileyguide.com/vets.html
   www.TAOnline.com

Additional websites to support returning service members:
   www.vba.va.gov/bin/vre/index/htm
   www.myhealth.va.gov
   www.oqp.med.va.gov/cpg/epg.htm
   www.vetsprevail.com
   www.pva.org
   www.usuhs.mil/psy/RFSMC.pdf
   helmetstohardhats.org
   prhome.defense.gov/
   www.homesforourtroops.org/site/PageServer
   www.triwest.com
   www.hand2handcontact.org
   www.hooah4health.com
   www.veteransoutreachcenter.org
   www.onefreedom.org
   www.militarymentalhealth.org
   www.thesoldiersproject.org
   www.giftfromwithin.com
   www.health.mil/inTransition
   www.pdhealth.mil

Resources for families: Strategic outreach to families:
   www.yellowribbon.mil
   www.ouhsc.edu/VetParenting/
   www.jointservicessupport.org/default.aspx
   www.sofarusa.org
   www.guardfamily.org
   www.sesameworkshop.org/initiatives/emotion/tlc
   apaperhug.com
   www.nmfa.org

www.cominghomeproject.net
www.afterdeployment.org
www.goldstarfamilysupport.com
www.fisherhouse.org
www.militarybenefits.com
www.militarymoney.com

Additional websites cited in this guidebook:
www.gamblersanonymous.com
cust-cf.apa.org/ptgi/
www.ppc.sas.upenn.edu
counsellingresource.com/quizzes/alcohol-mast/index.html
www.drinkerscheckup.com
rethinkingdrinking.niaaa.nih.gov
www.quitandrecovery.org
alcoholism.about.com/od/meetings/a/ann-e_app.htm
www.smartrecovery.com
www.niaaa.nih.gov
www.cpt.musc.edu
www.anxieties.com
www.mindful.org
www.umassmed.edu/Content.aspx?id=41252
www.griefnet.org
www.ajokeaday.com
www.beatingtheblues.co.uk
www.survivalartist.com
www.gratitudelog.com
www.theatre-of-war.com
www.TED.com
www.strongbonds.org
www.couplescoachingcouples.com
www.spousonomics.com
www.iceeft.com/
www.learningtoforgive.com
homepage.psy.utexas.edu/homepage/faculty/pennebaker/home2000/writingandhealth.
    html
www.livingoutthedream.org/
www.stickk.com/

Websites designed to help bolster resilience:
www.asu.edu/resilience
www.financialaidfinder.com/subsidized-vs-unsubsidized-stafford-loans.html
www.cstsonline.org
www.apa.org/helpcenter/

ACTION #82

Remember that "there is *no* situation so bad, that by my own actions, I cannot make it worse."

Here are some things I can do to make my situation *worse*. Here are things to watch out for:

I can ruminate, brood, actively suppress and avoid reminders, engage in safety behaviors that perpetuate and exacerbate personal distress, feel sorry for myself, blame myself, dwell on feelings on guilt, shame, anger, moral injury, clam up, keep secrets, avoid seeking help, engage in negative thinking, turn people off, view setbacks and failures as "end points," give up, use substances as a self-medication device. My doing these things will *increase my emotional pain and hurt the ones I love.*

ACTION #83

Instead, I can continue my "journey of healing" and view bumps in the road and detours as personal challenges and learning opportunities and *not* permit any lapses to become a full-blown relapse.

Useful Information

In the Chinese language, the concept of crisis is depicted by two characters (Wei Ji). The first character (Wei) represents danger, while the second character (Ji) represents opportunity. These two characters together connote the idea that a crisis situation is dangerous, but it also provides an opportunity for positive change.

Quotable Quotes

"*I have learned to view setbacks as learning opportunities.*"

"*I can create a 'Vision Statement' and add a 'Step-by-step Action Plan.'*"

"*I am my own living experiment.*"

ACTION #84

I use my action plans.

"*You can't throw a habit out the window; you have to coax it down the stairs, one step at a time.*"

—Mark Twain

With Mark Twain's advice in mind, what is my action plan to bolster my *re-silience*? I can choose a fitness area I wish to improve and fill out the following Action Plan. To be effective, an Action Plan needs to begin with a statement of my goals.

A "goal" is something I want to get or something I want to have happen and I am willing to work for it.

- My goal is:

- The change(s) I want to make are:

- The most important reasons for change are:

- The steps I plan to take in changing are/or the advice I would give someone else to achieve this goal is:

- How can I get started? What *small changes* can I make to begin with?

- The ways other people can help me achieve this goal are:
  - Person:
  - Possible ways they can help:

- I will *know* if my plan is working if:

- *Who else* will notice the change? What would he/she observe?

- Some things that could *interfere* with my plan are:

- Some solutions to those possible obstacles and potential road blocks are:

- What could be done *ahead of time*, be on the lookout for?

- What could be done when they occur?

- If my action plan does *not* work, I will:

- What are the pros and cons (short-term, intermediate, and long-term) of making these changes?

- I can write out this action plan and *share it* with someone else who is important to me. I can make a *public commitment* to change.

- I can *take credit* for my efforts and *reinforce* myself by:

ACTION #85

Here are other examples of ways to improve my behavioral fitness (Please email these suggestions *to examples@roadmaptoresilience.org*).

_____

_____

_____

_____

Spiritual Fitness

The word "spirituality" is derived from the Latin word "spirale," which means "to blow or breathe." The word "religion" is derived from the Latin word "re-ligare" which means "co- connect." One can pursue "spiritual fitness" *without* formally engaging in religious activities. Broadly defined, spirituality refers to connecting to something outside of self. Spirituality is your personal connection with meaning and purpose in your life through something greater than yourself. This could include a belief in a higher power of some type or a devotion to a set of deeply held personal beliefs and values. Spirituality can take many different forms and it *does not have to be tied* to being religious or believing in a higher power or God. Religion has been defined as a search for personal significance and meaning in ways related to sacred concepts and practices.

> "Viktor Frankl, who survived the Nazi death camp at Auschwitz, observed that it was not the youngest, strongest or even the smartest inmates who tended to survive. It was those who had found meaning in their lives. People, it turns out, need a reason to live."

> "Some 90% of the world's population engages in religious or spiritual practices which are a major means of coping with stress and illness."

> "God is like an attachment figure (a type of ideal parent) who fulfills the need for felt security."

> "I believe in God, only I spell it 'nature.'"

> —Frank Lloyd Wright

Spiritual fitness refers to one's search for a meaning and purpose in life. Spirituality provides a framework for meaning making and a sense of belongingness. For "believers" in a faith it is a way to search for benefits in traumatic events. Spirituality helps individuals implement their core values into social actions. Individuals who have a "why" to live for can bear with almost any traumatic events.

ACTION #86

I can use *positive religious ways of coping*. Ken Pargament has indicated that these include developing and maintaining a positive relationship with God or a higher power; collaborating with God in solving life's problems while maintaining a sense of personal control and self-confidence; accessing and using my religious social network as a resource; viewing my place of worship as a "safe haven." I can find some free time to recharge my "inner batteries."

Useful Information

Spiritual coping includes the adoption of faith-based beliefs and values as a form of positive coping. It also involves receiving support that draws upon common beliefs and values that nurture a sense of belongingness through participation in spiritual/faith-based groups and organizations. Such positive religious coping is associated with lower rates of stress, depression, anxiety and with increased levels of self-esteem, life satisfaction, physical and mental well-being and more satisfying interpersonal relationships. People who attend religious services regularly tend to live longer, are less likely to abuse alcohol and drugs and even go to the dentist more often than less religious folks.

Individuals who have a religious faith and who participate in religious services experience greater social supports resulting in reduced distress and increased personal growth. Such positive results have been found in parents who have lost a child as a result of suicide, cancer and burn patients and bereaved caregivers of HIV/AIDS patients.

Quotable Quotes

"My search for the sacred leads me to personal growth and resilience."

"Prayer reminds me that I am part of a community."

"There are no coincidences. Everything happens for a reason. God has his reasons."

"God never gives you more than you can handle. All that God does is for the best."

"I have to be better now because God was good to me so I have to be a good child of God."

"In Buddhism, originally founded by Siddharta Gutama, known as Buddha, one searches for self-enlightenment attained by an awakening to the Truth. The objective is to rid oneself of the tenacious idea that everything is everlasting. All is transitory."

"Life is regarded as continuous suffering. I can now see the positive side of suffering. Suffering will be redeemed."

"In the final analysis, the question of why bad things happen to good people translates itself into some very different questions, no longer asking why some-

thing happened, but asking how we will respond, what we intend to do now that it has happened?"
—Rabbi Harold Kushner, *Why Bad Things Happen to Good People*

"Crisis means a change in the flow of life. The river flows relentlessly to the sea. When it reaches a part that is blocked by rocks and debris, it struggles to find ways to continue its path. Would the alternative be to flow backwards? That is what a person in crisis craves, to go back in time. But life does not provide a reverse gear, and the struggle must be to go forward, like the river, with occasional pauses to tread water and check out where we are heading."

"When the roots of a tree hit a large stone or other obstacle, do they try to shove the stone away or crack it? No. The roots just grow around the obstacle and keep going. The stone may have interrupted or slowed the tree's growth for a while, but no stone, no matter how large can stop the tree from growing."

ACTION #87

I can make my situation worse and more distressing by using *negative religious ways of coping* that focus on themes of punishment and guilt. For example, I can hold the belief that God has abandoned me and is punishing me for wrongdoings of my sins; continually ask "why me" questions for which there are no answers; plead for miracles and God's intervention and defer responsibility and actions to God; relinquish to a higher power; have a "Spiritual Struggle," a "Soul Wound" and experience "moral injuries," feel guilty, ashamed and responsible for failures and losses. I can have a falling out with fellow congregants or with my clergy. Doing these things will increase my emotional pain and reduce my resilience. Instead, I can choose to use positive religious ways of coping (Also, see Action #86).

Quotable Quotes

Negative Religious Coping:

"My higher power failed me."

"I'm too bad to be loved by a higher power."

"How could there be a God given what I have seen?"

"God can't protect anybody."

"God isn't fair."

"I had a relationship with God before this traumatic event. After it, I never will again. I think He is a figment of man's imagination."

ACTION #88

I can use my faith to rekindle my sense of hope in myself and in others, and in the future. My faith reminds me that there is something more in life for me to do. I can unlock the benefits stemming from my spiritual beliefs.

Quotable Quotes

"Spirituality gives me strength. Even when I can't get to the point where I can get strength from it, I get hope from my faith and then when I get hope, I get strength."

"I was considering giving up and killing myself and I remembered the words of my Sunday School teacher who said if you get in trouble you can always call upon Jesus. That is what I did."

"I have learned to live in harmony with my destiny."

"My faith teaches that we all have within us the strengths and resources to overcome many of the effects of traumatic events and the ability to learn to manage whatever lingers. We each have the ability to rise above our circumstances."

"I realize how much life should be treasured."

"I now know that life is precious and should be savored. I realize how short time is."

"I have woken up now. I know what is really important to me, what I want, and who I am. I now know who my true friends are."

"Here today and gone tomorrow. You never know what each day is going to bring. I no longer waste my time worrying about the little things in my life."

"I feel more able to cope with what life throws at me."

"I am hopeful about my future and I look forward to new possibilities."

"I am so grateful to have people in my life who care for me and will help in my journey to resilience and growth."

Answering the following *Hinge Questions* can help nurture hope.

- "What would have to happen to help me be more hopeful about the future?"

- "What keeps me going in difficult times?"

- "Whom can I rely on during difficult times? Can my faith and spiritual beliefs help?"

- "What makes life worth living?"

ACTION #89

I visit the Chaplain or other clergy persons for assistance.

Useful Information

In the United States, 43% to 60% of people who have emotional problems turn *first* to clergy for help.

Prayer and faith are the most widely used methods of coping with traumatic life events. For example, 90% of Americans reported that after the September 11th terrorist attack, they turned to prayer, religion or some form of spiritual activities in an effort to cope.

85% of the world's population embrace some sort of religious beliefs. Adults tend to search for meaning, particularly during times of uncertainty.

ACTION #90

I seek inspiration, guidance and comfort from prayer, meditation, scripture reading, religious music, devotional activities, spiritual journal writing, and view my faith as part of my support network. I can join a religious group activity and volunteer to help with a community service project.

Useful Information

Contemplative traditions such as meditation and prayer are a form of mental exercise that change the circuits of the brain involved in the regulation of emotion and attention.

Quotable Quotes

"What sustains me is singing gospel songs like Amazing Grace and other hymns I learned as a child. I can picture the congregation singing and rocking and I am back there again. It helps to get me through."

"The first thing prayer does for us is put us in touch with other people who share the same concerns, values and dreams. Prayer redeems people from isolation. People pray as a way of talking out their fears without the embarrassment of having to say them out loud, and as a reassurance that they are not alone."
—Rabbi Harold Kushner, *When Bad Things Happen to Good People*

"I pray a lot and ask for strength and guidance, so I can stay on the straight and narrow path."

"My inspiration comes from putting my personal values into my day-to-day actions."

"My reading of scripture has taught me that life is meaningful by finding ways to matter to other people."

"It is all about giving back through community service."

ACTION #91

I participate in spiritual and religious groups, attend church, synagogue, mosque or some other religious site. I can develop a sense of belonging and gain inspiration through connection with others and access the social, emotional and material supports of church participants and clergy.

Quotable Quotes

"At first, I didn't think attending the spiritual group was for me, but the other group members were as skeptical as I was, and that helped me feel like maybe I belonged there after all. There are seven other group members and we came from different religious backgrounds Catholic, Protestant, Jewish, Evangelical and Islamic. We agreed that the group spirit is to value each individual's personal faith, so there is no 'right' set of beliefs. I found participating worthwhile."

"When we tell our own stories and listen to those of others, we come in touch with life, divinity and soul. Telling our story is a way of preserving our individual history and at the same time defining our place in the larger flow of events. Story telling knits the community together."

—Edward Tick, War and the Soul

"As soon as I let someone at my church know of my illness, there were people praying for me. It is hard not to feel valued and closer to people who are showing so much care for you."

ACTION #92

I engage in spiritual rituals like daily public prayers, a Native American Sweat Lodge service, Spiritual Meditation, Catholic Mass, Prayer Service, Rites of Passage Ceremony, Funeral or Memorial Services, play religious music to lift my spirit, read the Bible, perform good deeds and attend other religious services, and create a healing ritual. For example, find a place in my home or garden or somewhere else that I can designate as a "sacred" space and where I can make an offering.

Quotable Quotes

"In Islam, religious activities are highly visible in people's everyday life. Daily public praying creates the rhythm, harmony and security of daily life. Such spiritual sharing provides a religious explanatory model and an affiliation with others, a realization of one's own strength and recognition of new possibilities."

"When I was in a desperate mood, I sought consolation in praying to God Almighty. He consoled me and calmed me down, although I sometimes doubted whether God knows what is happening to us."

"I believe that I am on the path to God with whom I can achieve closeness in Paradise."

"When my grandmother died, because it was my first experience, I couldn't even collect her ashes. But that taught me to be steadfast, that I shouldn't slacken off. I felt as if I heard a voice from heaven telling me I should pay more heed to my close relations. And I'm so grateful of having caught the message that I change the water for our family Buddhist alter every morning, and put my hands flat together in prayer. You know, just for a couple of seconds. Before that I was self-centered; after that I just want to express my gratitude, that's all."

ACTION #93

I revisit the site of combat or memorial site and participate in commemorative services. I can maintain a psychological bond with those who have died.

Quotable Quotes

Bobby Kennedy gave a speech on the night of Martin Luther King's assassination and quoted the poet Aeschylus:
"He who learns must suffer. And even in our sleep pain that cannot forget, falls drop by drop upon the heart, and in our despair, against our will, comes wisdom to us by the awful grace of God."

"I feel grief for people. Anybody who has had a tragedy in their life, I can feel their pain."

"Thou shalt not forget is my first commandment. To forget is to dishonor."

"There is still one thing we can do for those we loved and lost. We could not keep them alive. Perhaps we could not even significantly lessen their pain, but the one crucial thing that we can do for them after their death is to let them be witnesses for God and for life. The dead depend on us for their redemption and their immortality."
—Rabbi Harold Kushner

ACTION #94

I can forgive others and forgive myself. Forgiveness is for the forgiver. It is about taking my life back and moving on in peace with a little more wisdom and compassion. Forgiveness releases restraints and ensures that our lives are not consumed or dominated by intense stubbornness, anger, hostility, guilt, shame and thoughts of revenge. Forgiveness is a way to set myself free; a way to get free of a past that may be keeping me locked in a cycle of self-destructive behavior. Forgiveness is a way to lighten my emotional load a day at a time; a way to stop beating myself up. Forgiveness is a journey that takes time. It is a deliberate effort to replace negative emotions of resentment, hostility, anger, hatred toward the aggressor(s) with positive emotions and compassion. It requires the ability to view behaviors from multiple perspectives and reduce the preoccupation with the desire for revenge.

Forgiveness does not condone the behavioral acts of a perpetrator, but it does help overcome the sense of being a victim. Instead of mentally replaying one's hurt, an individual can change his/her "grievous story" and seek other ways to achieve one's goals. Forgiveness is not reconciliation or a re-establishing of a relationship with the perpetrator(s). A person can forgive and still have painful feelings (Robert Enright, (2001).

Useful Information

The act of forgiveness, which is a *process*, not a one-time event, improves one's physical health, alleviates depression, lessens anger and lowers stress hormones and blood pressure, and improves relationship health. Forgiveness is the beginning of a journey of letting go that may take some time. One forgives to quiet their angry feelings, to alter destructive thoughts, to improve their relationships and to make peace with themselves. The important thing is to forgive in one's mind and heart.

People of faith often evidence forgiveness following a betrayal or a victimizing experience. For instance, the Amish of Lancaster, Pennsylvania attended the funeral of the man who committed suicide after murdering five girls in an Amish school house. Their faith guided them through the painful period of mourning. Another example of forgiveness by the Amish community came when a member of their church pulled off a Bernie Madoff Ponzi scheme that resulted in the loss of millions of dollars. For many Amish investors, they expressed a willingness to forgive.

But a *caution* about forgiveness needs to be kept in mind. Forgiveness is a process that can be either beneficial or harmful, depending upon the relationship in which it occurs. For example, women who were physically abused by their partner and who were forgiving were more likely to return to their abusive partner and put themselves at risk for re-victimization. The act of forgiveness should not blind one to the need to assess risk. In some situations forgiveness can contribute to increased marital satisfaction, while in other contexts the act of forgiveness can backfire. With this caveat in mind, let's consider ways to engage in acts of forgiveness.

How To: Engage in Forgiveness

- In order to *forgive* you must first tell the story of what happened, grieve it fully and then turn away from grudges, bitterness, and the kind of ruminating that amplifies the story and gives it too much replay time. Give up the need for revenge, but seek a just resolution.

- Recognize that *forgiveness* is a form of enlightened self-interest, a gift that you give yourself by learning whatever good lessons you can from an event.

  "Life is not fair, so get over thinking that it should be. Bad things happen to good people all the time. But as Stephen Post and his colleagues have noted, "'Good things also happen to good people, who forgive, share and give back'" (Post, et al, 2007).

- Think of someone you have forgiven or who has forgiven you in the past. What did you/he/she do? What did you/he/she say and not say? Can you use any of these strategies with others or on yourself? You are in charge of your rate of healing, your journey to resilience and personal growth.

- Consider the following. Your best friend comes to you and admits to you that he/she has done something of which he/she is very ashamed. He/she is not able to "undo" what happened. He/she feels alone and afraid. He/she feels very guilty and thinks he/she should be punished forever for what he/she has done (or failed to do). He/she wants you to do the punishing. What would you do? What would you say? How would you decide? If you are feeling guilty or ashamed about something that you did or did not do would you use any of this advice on yourself?

A Forgiveness Exercise

1. Write down the name of someone who has hurt you in a significant way.

2. What has this person done or not done to hurt you?

3. What is keeping you from forgiving this person? What are the costs and benefits that contribute to your *stubbornness* to forgive and move on?

4. What are the pros and cons, the potential benefits, of reaching out to this person?

5. What would this person need to do to earn your forgiveness?

6. What would you do to foster the forgiveness process with this person? What is one small first step you can take (a call, a letter, an email, ask an intermediary person to communicate your wishes, send a card, gift,

flowers, arrange for a meeting, and the like)? In what ways can you show that you are a *bigger person*?

- What have you done to make peace *with yourself* in order to come to terms with your hurt, anger, stubbornness?

- Complete the following sentences:

  - *"Someone I will have to make amends to is . . ."*

  - *"Someone from whom I would like forgiveness is . . ."*

  - *"If I forgive myself and show compassion, I will no longer feel . . ."*

  - *"If I forgive myself (and others), it means that . . ."*

  - *"If I forgive myself and others, my relationships will . . ."*

  - *"One way I can stop 'beating myself up' is to . . ."*

  - *"I can stop holding grudges against others and myself by . . ."*

- Beware of what Janis Abrams Spring has called "cheap forgiveness" in her book, *How Can I Forgive You?*, which is characterized as offering a quick and easy pardon with no processing of emotion and no coming to terms with the injury. This may take the form of a superficial, unilateral pardon and an attempt at peacekeeping. Cheap forgiveness may preserve the relationship, but not lead to reconciliation.

  - "Is it worth it to harbor grudges forever?"

  - "What is the impact, the toll, the price you and others pay for your stubbornness to not forgive, for your failure of compassion and acceptance? Is this the price you want to pay?"

Visit the website *www.learningtoforgive.com*.

Quotable Quotes

"Holding onto anger is like grasping a hot coal with the intent of throwing it at someone else; you are the one who gets burned."

—The Buddha

"Our brain is hard wired to remember painful events. But we do not have to forget in order to forgive."

"The ability to forgive and the ability to love are the weapons God has given us to enable us to live fully, bravely and meaningfully in this less-than-perfect world."
—Rabbi Harold Kushner

"Forgiveness has been found to produce benefits for the forgiver leading to a lasting inner peace. Forgiving does not mean condoning the other person's actions, nor minimizing the hurt that those actions caused. If you decided to forgive, there is good reason to believe that you will feel much better in the long run. It is in your hands and no one else's-that may be the real power of forgiveness."
—Robert Nay, Taking Charge of Anger

"Forgiveness and acceptance are a form of self-care, a generous and healing gift to oneself, accomplished by the self for the self."
—Janis Abrams Spring

ACTION #95

Use "self-compassion" and "loving kindness" meditations and activities toward myself and toward others. I learn to walk away from hate and the desire for revenge. Instead, I can engage in a Loving-Kindness Meditation (LKM) and Compassion Meditation (CM) towards others, as well as toward myself. The LKM aims to develop an emotional state of unconditional kindness to people. The CM is designed to cultivate compassion or sympathy for those stricken with misfortune. I can work on creating a mental kindness to all beings, including myself. Self-directed self-compassion toward my own suffering, being mindful when considering negative aspects of myself and recognizing my shared humanity can enhance *resilience*. Cultivating self-compassion and self-acceptance in response to self-critical thoughts by envisioning forms of loving kindness (good deeds), can engender well-being and resilience.

Preliminary neuroendocrine studies indicate that practicing and engaging in LKM and CM can reduce stress and improve immune responses. Individuals engage in *self-compassion* by envisioning the type of person they want to be, rather than berating themselves for failures, quelling their "inner critic" and developing the capacity for self-soothing and self-nurturing acts of understanding and kindness toward themselves. Individuals high in self-compassion tend to see their fallibilities and weaknesses as part of the larger human condition ('Not alone in struggling with flaws and failures'), and recognizing their connections with others. In contrast, individuals low in self-compassion tend to avoid thinking about weaknesses and failures or they engage in "tunnel vision" that prevents deep experiencing of the present moment. Such avoidant behaviors intensify negative emotions; sacrifices self-understanding and can contribute to self isolation.

Individuals high in self-compassion tend to have greater life satisfaction, higher emotional intelligence, greater social connectedness, less anxiety and depression, less fear of failure, lower job burnout and higher well-being.

The following are suggestions on ways to enhance your level of self-compassion.:

1. Try a self-directed Compassionate Mind Training exercise. Envision a friend or relative who is in the same situation you are in. He or she has come to you for help. Think about ways you could listen non-judgmentally and *with compassion*. What would you say? What would you do? Could you use the same understanding, kindness, warmth, and support toward yourself that you would offer your friend or relative? Can you introduce your "Compassionate Self" to your "Suffering Self?" Think about ways to move forward without self-blaming, self-criticizing and self-injurious behaviors? You are in charge of your rate of progress, your journey to resilience and personal growth.

2. Be patient and non-judgmental toward aspects of yourself. Be kinder toward yourself. Self-criticism engenders isolation.

3. Use visualization to further develop self-compassion. View yourself as a kind and caring person toward others and toward yourself. Accept negative feelings and take actions, despite them. Challenge your self-judgmental "toxic beliefs," learn to tolerate, acknowledge, label and embrace any thoughts and feelings, rather than react to or avoid them. In fact, there is a psychotherapy approach called Acceptance and Commitment Therapy that teaches these mindfulness skills.

4. Finally, when can acts of kindness toward self and others have *harmful effects*? If individuals are too committed to engaging in acts of kindness, they may avoid providing criticism, negative feedback during conflict and problem-solving situations. The constructive feedback about specific bothersome partner behaviors, especially during disputes, has been found to contribute to long-term marital satisfaction. In an attempt to be kind, individuals may "sweep contentious issues under the rug" and avoid bringing up issues, thus, putting their relationship in jeopardy. When acts of unkindness are met with conscientious efforts to learn from and correct interpersonal mistakes, they have the potential to contribute to interpersonal well-being.

Quotable Quotes

"Opportunities to find deep powers within ourselves come when life seems most challenging."

—Joseph Campbell

"I have learned the meaning of suffering."

"I felt so burdened by hatred and a drive for revenge. I gradually came to understand that if I really wanted to be free in my heart, I needed to learn to forgive others, as well as myself."

ACTION #96

I find comfort and security, a sense of peace and acceptance in my religious beliefs, like afterlife, reincarnation, the presence of the spirit or soul of those who have died. I can construct a Spiritual Family Tree highlighting the ancestral history of spiritual and religious traditions in my family or cultural group. I can write an "epitaph" of what I want to be remembered for. Address the following *Hinge Questions*:

- At the end of your life, when you look back, what will mean the most to you?

- What do you want your legacy to be?

- Write an obituary of yourself that you would feel proud of.

Quotable Quotes

"My life is my message."

—Mahatma Gandhi

"When we are no longer able to change a situation- we are challenged to change ourselves."

—Viktor Frankl

"Do not conform to the pattern of the word, but be transformed by the renewing of your mind. Then you will be able to test and approve what God's will is—his good, pleasing and perfect will."
—Paul's call to Roman Christians—Romans 12:2

ACTION #97

I can discuss the spiritual meaning of my trauma experiences and my military experiences with others who care about me; harvest the lessons that I have learned and share them with others. I hold the belief that my trauma and military experiences made my faith stronger. My faith gives me a sense of direction in my life that feels meaningful.

Useful Information

Many returning service members have reported feeling strengthened by their faith. Meaning is not something out there that is given to us; it is something we give to ourselves. We do that through stories.

Quotable Quotes

"My faith provides a true North Star that orients me when I am lost in a sea of change and desperation."

"This is God's way of testing me (us)."

"Feel purified by fire."

"This is God's way of teaching me about the preciousness of life."

"I have been able to draw on my religion in dealing with everyday problems."

"My story of resilience can be a lighthouse of hope to others."

"I recognize that no man is an island which means every person has significance and importance to others."

"Religion is my way of out-sourcing my spiritual well-being to a supernatural expert."

"I now feel part of a larger social organization."

ACTION #98

I can address any "moral injuries" or "soul wounds," sense of guilt or shame I experienced as a result of my deployment or traumatic experience.

Useful Information

Some service members have found it helpful to address their "personal hurt," their "moral injuries" and "soul wounds", and accompanying feelings of guilt, shame, and anger by using an empty chair exercise" (See Action #34). Using their imagination, the service members can have a conversation with another person for whom they have great respect or with a moral popular authority figure.

The service members tell the imagined moral authority figure what has changed in them and their behavior since the distressing deployment events. They describe the impact of any guilt, shame, and/or anger on their life and on the lives of loved ones. The service members are asked to consider what the moral authority figure would say to them after hearing what has just been said. The service members can switch roles and now assume the advice-giving moral authority figure. This conversation is to be conducted in the present tense. What "wise" and "supportive" advice would be offered? Is there anyway the service members could use such guidance?

An alternative procedure that has been used to help service members address the need for personal forgiveness and compassion is to ask them to use the "empty chair exercise," but this time imagine they are speaking to someone for whom they feel protective like a younger brother or junior comrade. They are asked to imagine that particular person confessing to guilt and shame-engendering actions and the emotional aftermath. The service members are asked to consider what they would say. The empty-chair exercise (also see Action #34) can help the service members develop "healing stories" and *resilience*.

ACTION #99

I reset my "moral compass" and refocus on my core values, beliefs and life aspirations. I can call upon my warrior ethos that I was trained to use. Remember the seven core values, "loyalty, duty, respect, selfless service, honor, integrity, and personal courage," cited in the US Army Field Manual. "These values are ingrained in me and no matter what happens when I am deployed, they will never be lost. This is what I am bringing home with me." I knew my best chance of staying alive was keeping my buddies alive. I became my "brother's keeper." I was steeped in a culture of courage, comradeship of a deep and everlasting bond.

Useful Information

When treatments are helpful to returning service members with PTSD and related difficulties, these interventions work in large part by helping them retrieve positive memories and use coping strategies that are in competition with negative memories. Treatment helps returning warriors appreciate the strengths, courage, adaptability and *resilience* that they brought home from deployment.

Quotable Quotes

"*Courage requires knowing and feeling the anguish of loss.*"

—Aristotle

"*The happy warrior is diligent to learn and abides by his resolve and stops not there. He is able to endure as more exposed to suffering and distress; thence more alive to tenderness.*"
—William Wordsworth (as cited by Nancy Sherman, 2010)

"*As a result of this traumatic experience, I have learned that I have to get my 'moral muscles' in shape by exercising them regularly.*"

"*Let me tell you some of the positive things about being in Iraq. I developed deep friendships and I know I would choose to die to protect my buddies and they*" *would do the same for me. I had a powerful sense of mission and purpose. I was able to help those in need. Saving lives, playing with the kids, helping build a school, giving out meds, these are some of things that stay with me."*

—Anonymous Service Member

"The men who fought the Battle of Midway in World War II had no right to win. Yet they did, and in doing so they changed the course of the war . . . even against the greatest of odds. There is something in the human spirit—a magic blend of skill, faith and valor—that can lift men from certain defeat to incredible victory."

—Walter Lord (1993)

What did you bring home from your deployment? These resilient skills can be called upon to deal with the challenges of reintegration. It is like learning to ride a two wheel bike. You may not bike ride for a long time, but you never quite forget. You may get rusty or forget you have these skills, but your balance can be called upon and be redeveloped.

Can you give examples of each of these survival behaviors and values you brought home from deployment?

The values that contribute to the foundation for resilience are described in the acronym "H-SLIDER."

H—*Honor means*: Hard work; Honesty; Humility; Hardiness; Withstanding of hardships

S—*Selfless Service means*: Sacrifice; Subordinate self to the group; Courage and accountability to one's comrades which is more powerful than self; Preservation/self-regulation/self-reliance/self-discipline/self-reflection and a sense of purpose; Devotion to Duty, Teamwork and Pride

L—*Loyalty means*: Brotherhood; Closeness; Commitment to your unit; Development of a "Band of Brothers/Sisters" bond; Values and traditions of warriorhood; Identification with group, service and country; Positive effects due to feelings of belongingness; Strong bonds and camaraderie with those who have served; Looking out for others; Leadership and teamwork

I—*Integrity means*: Grit; Leadership; Commitment to a higher cause; Patriotism

D—*Duty means*: Dedication; Determination; Discipline; Sense of Responsibility to others; Commitment to mission accomplishment; Tactical awareness; Mental focus and learned safety habits; Ability to be clear-minded, strategic, alert, pro-active and optimistic

E—*Excellence means*: Bravery; Confidence; Controlled aggression; Adaptability; Valor; Knowledge of how precious and fragile life is; Development of a broader perspective on life

R—*R*espect means: Readiness; Responsibility; Robustness and resilience

Remember the Warrior Ethos:

I will always place the Mission first.
I will never accept defeat.
I will never quit.
I will never leave a fallen comrade.

Your answers to the following *Hinge Questions* address how these values have become part of you, been internalized, and can guide your reintegration process and bolster your *resilience*.

- "What core values and strengths did you develop as a member of the military?"

- "How can these core values and your strengths contribute to your mission of reintegrating into civilian life, ongoing service, and to your reaching your personal goals?"

- "How are you using your core values and strengths to build strong relationships?"

- "Which of these core values do you wish to instill in your children and other family members?"

- "How can you help your fellow citizens develop and practice these core values?"

- "How can you make a 'gift' of these core values to others?"

- Can you give examples of each of the "H-SLIDER" values and skills that you brought home from deployment or that you developed as a result of your trauma experience?

ACTION #100

I recognize that life is short and I want to get the most out of every moment I have. I commit myself to living each moment fully. I can begin a stage of what is called *generativity* in which I care and have a concern for others, and especially for future generations. I can work together with my spiritual faith in formulating and implementing a plan.

ACTION #101

Here are other examples of ways to improve my spiritual fitness (Please email these suggestions to *examples@roadmaptoresilience.org*).

_____

_____

_____

_____

Conclusions

Psychological Characteristics
of Resilient Individuals

You are at a "narrative fork" in the road. Which path will you take?

Bolster Positive Supportive Relationships

Reconnect with social supports. Ask for help when needed. Share emotions and stories of survival. Renegotiate roles and responsibilities at home. Access resources.

Experience Positive Emotions and Regulate Strong Negative Emotions

Be realistically optimistic, hopeful, have humor, and the ability to laugh at oneself, face one's fears and manage emotions. Have positive expectations about the future, a positive self-image. Build on existing strengths, talents and social supports.

Adopt a Task-Oriented Coping Style

Ability to match coping skills with the demands of the situation. Some situations that are potentially changeable call for direct-action problem-solving skills. Some situations are *not* changeable and they call for acceptance and emotional regulatory palliative coping skills. Avoid avoidance.

Cognitively Flexible

Ability to reframe, re-define, re-story, find benefits, engage in social problem-solving and alternative thinking to adaptively meet changing demands and handle transitional stressors.

Undertake a Meaning-Making Mission

Create meaning and a purpose in life; survivor's mission. Use faith, spirituality and values as a "moral compass." Be altruistic and make a "gift" of experience. Share one's story. General sense of trust in others.

Keep Fit and Safe

Exercise, follow a routine, reduce risks, and avoid unsafe high-risk behaviors (smoking, substance abuse, chasing "adrenaline rush" activities in an unsafe manner).

Psychological Characteristics of Individuals Who "Get Stuck" and Show Evidence of Ongoing Distress and Adjustment Problems

If we can determine what factors contribute to persistent and chronic PTSD and related adjustment difficulties, then we can figure out what leads individuals to get "stuck." We can then determine how to help these individuals get "unstuck" and develop *resilience*. Let us consider what factors come into play at the cognitive, emotional, behavioral and spiritual levels. *How many of these activities do you engage in?*

At the Thinking Level

- Engage in self-focused, "mental defeating" type of thinking. There is a perception that one has lost autonomy as a human being, lost the will to exert control and maintain identity, lost the belief that one has a "free will." See self as a "victim", controlled by uninvited thoughts, feelings and circumstances, continually vulnerable, unlovable, and undesirable, unworthy. Use dramatic metaphors that reinforce this style of thinking. "I am a prisoner of the past," "entrapped," "contaminated," "damaged goods," "a doormat," "an outsider." Experience a form of mental exhaustion, mental weariness.

- Hold erroneous beliefs that changes are permanent, the world is unsafe, unpredictable and that people are untrustworthy. Hold a negative, foreshortened view of the future and the belief that life has lost its meaning.

- Engage in self-berating, self-condemnation, self-derogatory "story-telling" to oneself and to others (i.e., self blame, guilt-engendering hindsight, biased thinking; anger-engendering thoughts of viewing provocations as being done "on purpose").

- Engage in upward social comparisons, so one compares poorly in one's coping abilities. Be preoccupied with what others think of them. Engage in comparison of self versus others; before versus now; now versus what might have been.

- Ruminate repeatedly, dwell on, focus upon, brood, pine over loses, "near miss" experiences. Replay over and over your concerns about the causes, consequences and symptoms related to negative emotions and losses. Use repetitive thinking cycles ("loss spiral"). Hold the belief that one cannot do anything to control such thoughts. ("My thoughts are like a movie that never stops." "This is like a form of self-punishment that I deserve."). Focus on your regrets.

- Engage in contra-factual thinking, repeatedly asking "Why me" and "If only" questions for which there are no satisfactory answers.

- Engage in avoidant thinking processes of deliberately suppressing thoughts, using distracting behaviors, using substances; avoidant coping behaviors and dissociation ("spaced out" behaviors). Fear memories and accompanying feelings and engage in avoidant behaviors. Fail to challenge fears; do not "invite them to tea."

The more one attempts to suppress cognitive material, the more that material intrudes into consciousness, like a boomerang rebound effect. The act of avoiding traumatic memories given their aversive qualities, results in intensifying re-experiencing symptoms, particularly intrusive memories, flashbacks and nightmares.

- Have an over generalized memory (scattered and lacking coherence) and recall style which intensifies hopelessness and impairs problem-solving, as well as difficulty remembering specific positive experiences. Memories are fragmented, sensory driven and fail to integrate traumatic events into autobiographical memory or narrative. Let the traumatic events define who they are.

- Engage in "thinking traps." For example, tunnel vision as evidenced in the failure to believe anything positive could result from trauma experience; confirmatory bias as evidenced in the failure to retrieve anything positive about one's self-identity; or recall any positive coping memories of what one did to survive, or what one is still able to accomplish "in spite of" victimization; do mind-reading, over generalizing, personalizing, jumping to conclusions, catastrophizing; "sweating the small stuff" and emotional reasoning such as viewing failures and lapses as "end points."

- Evidence "stuckness" in one's thinking processes and behavior. Respond to new situations in post-deployment settings "as if" one was still in combat (misperceive threats).

At the Emotional Level

- Engage in emotional avoidance strategies ("Pine over losses", deny or shift your feelings, clam up, bury emotions and do not consider the possible consequences of doing so).

- Magnify and intensify fears and anger.

- Experience guilt (hindsight bias or Monday-morning quarterbacking), shame, complicated grief, demoralization, loss of hope.

- Fail to engage in grief work that honors and memorializes loved ones or buddies who were lost.

- Fail to share or disclose feelings, fail to process traumatic memories. Focus on "hot spots" and "stuck points."

At the Behavioral Level

- Engage in avoidant behaviors of trauma-related feelings, thoughts, reminders, activities and situations; engage in dissociating behaviors.

- Be continually hyper vigilant, overestimating the likelihood and severity of danger. Act as if one is on "sentry duty" all the time. Act like a faulty smoke detector that goes off at the slightest signal.

- Engage in safety behaviors that interfere with the disconfirmation of emotional beliefs and the processing ("restorying") of trauma-related memories and beliefs.

- Engage in delay seeking behaviors. Avoid seeking help. Keep secrets, stuff feelings and be stubborn and rigid.

- Engage in high risk-taking behaviors; chasing the "adrenaline rush" in an unsafe fashion; put self at risk for revictimization.

- Engage in health-compromising behaviors (smoking, substance abuse as a form of self-medication, lack of exercise, sleep disturbance that goes untreated, poor diet, dependence on energy drinks, and abandonment of healthy behavioral routines).

- Engagement in self-handicapping behaviors ("excuse-making").

- Use passive, disengaged coping behaviors, social withdrawal, resigned acceptance, wishful thinking and emotional distancing.

At the Social Level

- Withdraw, isolate oneself, detach from others.

- Perceive self as being unwanted, a "burden," distrusting others and having feelings of thwarted belongingness. ("No one cares." "No one understands." "No one can be trusted.")

- Associate with peers and family members who reinforce and support maladaptive behaviors. Put self in high-risk situations.

- Have family members who are "enablers" and who protect them from exposure situations that can combat avoidance behaviors and who make excuses for them, or who inadvertently, unwittingly, and perhaps unknowingly, reinforce their maladaptive behaviors.

- Experience an unsupportive and indifferent social environment (i.e., individuals who are critical, intrusive, and unsympathetic and who offer "moving on" statements such as "You will get over this. Time heals everything.")

- Fail to seek social support or help, such as peer-related groups, chaplain services, or professional assistance.

At the Spiritual Level

- Fail to use faith or religion as a means of coping.

- Have a "spiritual struggle" and view God as having punished and abandoned them.

- Use *negative* spiritual coping responses. Relinquish actions to a higher power, pleas for miracles or divine intervention; become angry with God; be demanding.

- Experience "moral injuries" that compromise values. Lose "moral compass" and "shatter" deeply held beliefs in safety, trust, and self-worth; experience a "soul wound."

- Avoid contact with religious members who can be supportive.

Keep in mind that post-trauma distress and resilience can co-exist, but one can take specific *Action Steps* to increase the likelihood of becoming more resilient. Which road will you take? What small first steps can you take to become more resilient?

Ways to Successfully Reintegrate and Become More Resilient

AREAS OF FITNESS	DOS	DON'TS
Physical	Take care of your health and body; Engage in health-promoting behaviors	Overlook health and abuse your body; Avoid exercise
Interpersonal	Nurture positive relationships (Reconnect, Share, Renegotiate Roles)	Isolate; Withdraw; Avoid help
Emotional	Experience ratio of 3 positive to 1 negative emotion; Take steps to emotional fitness using opposite actions, mindfulness, relaxation, facing fears and grieving	Behave in ways that escalate and maintain a "negative emotional spiral"
Thinking	Adopt a resilient mindset; Be psychologically flexible; Be optimistic, hopeful (benefit finding and remembering); Avoid "thinking traps"	Engage in negative thinking
Behavioral	Restore regular, safe routines; Access information; Show gratitude; Use "action plans;" Show grit; Seek assistance	Engage in "high-risk" activities
Spiritual	Use an active style of coping (problem solving and acceptance strategies); Use positive spiritual/religious ways of coping; Engage in a meaning-making mission; Reset your "moral compass;" Forgive yourself and others	Use avoidant style of coping (ignoring, suppressing or distracting); Use negative spiritual/religious coping strategies

Appendix A

Resilience Checklist: My Personal Resilience Plan: Creating a Vision of the Future

In each of the following fitness areas, identify the specific things you plan to do in order to improve your level of *resilience*. The number refers to the Action Plan # for each item, followed by the page number in the book. Check off those that you wish to focus on. How much confidence do you have that you will be able to follow through on each resilience-bolstering behavior?

Physical Fitness

_____ #1. (p.27) Take care of my body.

_____ #2. (p.28) Exercise regularly.

_____ #3. (p.30) Get quality sleep.

_____ #4. (p.33) Eat healthy.

_____ #5. (p.34) Avoid mood-altering drugs or overuse of alcohol.

_____ #6. (p.37) Use healthy coping procedures—engage *nature*.

_____ #7. (p.38) Avoid high-risk dangerous behaviors.

_____ #8. (p.39) Other examples of ways I can *keep physically fit*.

Interpersonal Fitness

_____ #9. (p.41) Recognize that deployment changes everyone and that readjustment takes time.

_____ #10. (p.43) Reconnect with social supports.

191

_____ #11. (p.44) Lean on others and seek and accept help.

_____ #12. (p.46) Give back and help others. Share my "islands of competence" with others.

_____ #13. (p.48) Participate in a social network.

_____ #14. (p.48) Share my emotions with someone I trust.

_____ #15. (p.49) How To: Improve Communication Skills

_____ #16. (p.52) How To: Be a Good Social Problem-solver

_____ #17. (p.52) How To: Improve my Conflict Management Skills

_____ #18. (p.54) How To: Nurture My Relationship with my partner or spouse

_____ #19. (p.58) Overcome barriers to seeking help.

_____ #20. (p.61) Use community resources such as websites, telephone hotlines.

_____ #21. (p.62) Use my cultural or ethnic traditions, rituals and identity as a support aide.

_____ #22. (p.62) Find a role model or mentor.

_____ #23. (p.63) Be proud of the mission that I served with my "Band of Brothers/Sisters."

_____ #24. (p.64) Use pets to maintain and develop relationships and as a way to manage moods.

_____ #25. (p.64) Other examples of ways to develop and use relationships.

Emotional Fitness

Ways to Increase Positive Emotions

_____ #26. (p.66) Cultivate positive emotions (use hobbies and pleasurable activities).

_____ #27. (p.68) Make a "bucket list" of emotional uplifting activities and then *just do it!*

_____ #28. (p.71) Show "grit"—ability to pursue with determination long-term goals (*"Choose hard right over easy wrong."*).

_____ #29. (p.73) Use positive humor.

_____ #30. (p.74) Express gratitude.

Ways to Regulate Negative Emotions

_____ #31. (p.76) Use "opposite actions" to cope with intense emotions.

_____ #32. (p.77) Give myself permission to experience and share emotions (feel sad, cry, grieve, become angry).

_____ #33. (p.79) Face my fears.

_____ #34. (p.80) Engage in constructive grieving (memorialize and honor those who have been lost).

_____ #35. (p.83) Share my story and the "rest of my story" of what led me to survive (share lessons learned).

_____ #36. (p.84) Handle and overcome my "emotional pain" that comes with feelings of being disconnected.

_____ #37. (p.85) Journal—use "writing cure."

_____ #38. (p.88) Use creative and expressive activities to work through my feelings.

_____ #39. (p.89) Enjoy the benefits of self-disclosure.

_____ #40. (p.89) *Re-story* my life and share evidence of my *resilience.*

_____ #41. (p.93) How To: Use Relaxation and Mindfulness Skills

_____ #42. (p.100) Change my self-talk.

_____ #43. (p.101) Engage in non-negative thinking and become more *stress-hardy*

_____ #44. (p.104) Other examples of ways to improve my emotional fitness.

Thinking Fitness

_____ #45. (p.105) Be psychologically flexible.

_____ #46. (p.107) Use constructive thinking and consider alternative solutions/pathways.

_____ #47. (p.108) Establish achievable goals.

_____ #48. (p.110) Establish realistic expectations.

_____ #49. (p.111) Look at things differently.

_____ #50. (p.112) Use hope to achieve goals.

_____ #51. (p.114) Be realistically optimistic and goal-directed.

_____ #52. (p.116) Bolster a sense of self- confidence and self-efficacy.

_____ #53. (p.117) Engage in benefit-finding ("Search for the silver lining.").

_____ #54. (p.119) Engage in benefit-remembering.

_____ #55. (p.119) Engage in downward comparison (consider those less fortunate).

_____ #56. (p.120) Go on a "meaning making mission." List and share positive military experiences with others.

_____ #57. (p.121) Engage in altruistic (helping) behaviors.

_____ #58. (p.122) Engage in "pass forward" and move toward "post-traumatic growth."

_____ #59. (p.123) Consider the lessons learned that I can share with others.

_____ #60. (p.124) Be mindful, "mentalize" and stay in the present.

_____ #61. (p.125) Associate with people who share my positive values in life and help me re-author my story.

_____ #62. (p.126) Use my "Change Talk", the language of "hope" and "becoming," and my RE-verbs.

_____ #63. (p.129) Avoid debilitating guilt and shame reactions.

_____ #64. (p.131) Avoid "thinking traps."

_____ #65. (p.136) Nurture a positive view of myself, others and the future.

_____ #66. (p.138) Create a "healing story."

_____ #67. (p.144) Other examples of ways to improve my thinking fitness.

Behavioral Fitness

_____ #68. (p.145) Develop safe regular routines.

_____ #69. (p.146) Stay calm under pressure. Keep my cool.

_____ #70. (p.148) Prepare for possible high-risk situations.

_____ #71. (p.149) Break tasks into doable subtasks.

_____ #72. (p.151) Avoid avoidance and accept, tolerate, confront and experience past traumatic events. Get unstuck from the past.

_____ #73. (p.152) Improve my "people-picking" skills. Avoid people, places and things that get me into trouble.

_____ #74. (p.153) Take a "news holiday."

_____ #75. (p.153) Co-exist with my difficult memories and use positive emotions to *undo* negative memories.

_____ #76. (p.153) Self-disclose to a trusted person.

_____ #77. (p.154) Join a social group that gives my life a sense of purpose.

_____ #78. (p.154) Establish a "new normal." Renegotiate my role and responsibilities.

_____ #79. (p.154) Adopt a "can do" attitude.

_____ #80. (p.155) Read to find comfort.

_____ #81. (p.156) Gather information (visit websites).

_____ #82. (p.160) Avoid making things "worse."

_____ #83. (p.160) Continue my "journey of healing" and view setbacks as "learning opportunities."

_____ #84. (p.160) Use my "action plans" and "backup plans."

_____ #85. (p.162) Other examples of ways to improve my behavioral fitness.

Spiritual Fitness

_____ #86. (p.163) Use *positive* religious/spiritual ways of coping.

_____ #87. (p.165) Avoid using *negative* religious/spiritual ways of coping.

_____ #88. (p.166) Rekindle *hope.*

_____ #89. (p.167) Visit the chaplain or some other clergy person for assistance.

_____ #90. (p.167) Use some form of spiritual/religious/devotional activities.

_____ #91. (p.168) Participate in a spiritual and religious group.

_____ #92. (p.168) Engage in spiritual/religious rituals.

_____ #93. (p.169) Engage in commemorative services.

_____ #94. (p.170) Forgive others and forgive oneself.

_____ #95. (p.173) Use "self-compassion" and "loving-kindness" meditations toward others and toward oneself.

_____ #96. (p.175) Use my spiritual/religious beliefs and traditions to find comfort and peace of mind.

_____ #97. (p.175) Share the spiritual lessons learned from my trauma experiences and deployment.

_____ #98. (p.176) Address my "moral injuries" and "soul wounds."

_____ #99. (p.177) Reset my "moral compass" and refocus on my core values and attitudes that I brought home from my deployment (H-SLIDER).

_____ #100. (p.179) Recognize life is short and commit to living each moment fully and enter a stage of "generativity"—give to future generations.

_____ #101. (p.180) Other examples of ways to improve my spiritual fitness.

My Resilience Action Plan

Now that I have reviewed the checklist of Resilience-enhancing activities, I need to identify 2 areas in which I can bolster or "grow" my resilience. Two specific Resilience-bolstering behaviors I want to work on are:

1. _____

2. _____

Now I can develop a personal "Action Plan" to strengthen my *resilience* (See Action #84).

In order to help me achieve my personal goals, I can visit the website *www.stickK.com* that provides a "game plan" on how to change my behavior and accomplish my goals. This website uses a Commitment Contract which builds in monitoring, public accountability and consequences.

After accomplishing my personal goals, I can retake the self-assessment of my Resilience. In what areas have I improved? See *cust-cf.apa.org/ptgi/* for the APA Help Center Post Traumatic Growth Inventory.

Appendix B
User-Friendly Guide of Resilient Behaviors

Another way to access information to bolster your *resilience* is offered in this Appendix. This is a quick way to find information "on demand" about a variety of specific areas. The specific challenges are arranged in alphabetical order (see words in italics) so you can scan down the list and find the page number on which the "How To" information is located. For example, if you are looking for information on ways to *communicate* more effectively, or on ways to learn to *relax*, or ways to improve *sleep* and the like, then just go to that item and you can find where in the book you can locate that information. Feel free to copy any of these "How To" steps and share then with others. Check off those items on the following list on which you would like to focus.

_____ (p.197) Create my Resilience *Action Plan*

_____ (p.34)   Reduce *Alcohol Intake*

_____ (p.121) Be more *Altruistic* (give back)

_____ (p.134) Control my *Anger*

_____ (p.151) Avoid *Avoidance*

_____ (p.58)   Develop a *"Can Do"* attitude

_____ (p.126) Use my *Change Talk* and *Language of Becoming*
          (p.127) How To: Us My RE-Verbs

_____ (p.49)   *Communicate* more effectively
          (p.49) How To: Improve Communication Skills

_____ (p.52)   How To: Improve my *Conflict Management Skills*
          (p.53) How To: Handle Inevitable Conflicts with Your Partner or
                Spouse

_____ (p.146) Use *Coping* Self-Statements
        (p.147) How To: Use Positive Coping Self-Statements

_____ (p.35) Assess my *Drinking* Behavior
        (p.34) What Is Your Drinking Pattern?
        (p.35) Do You Drink Too Much?
        (p.36) Safe Drinking Tips

_____ (p.33) *Eat* Healthier

_____ (p.90) *Exercise* More

_____ (p.165) Use my *Faith*:
        (p.163) Use Positive Spiritual Coping Skills
        (p.165) Avoid Using Negative Spiritual Coping Behaviors

_____ (p.79) Face My *Fears*

_____ (p.165) Use *Forgiveness* of Others and Self
        (p.171) How To: Engage in Forgiveness

_____ (p.108) Do *Goal Setting* (Set "S.M.A.R.T. Goals")

_____ (p.74) How To: Steps to Improve My Level of *Gratitude* and Make
        Gratitude a Daily Habit

_____ (p.80) Do *Grief Work*

_____ (p.129) Handle *Guilt and Shame*

_____ (p.66) Increase *Happiness*

_____ (p.138) Create a *"Healing Story"*

_____ (p.44) Ask for *Help*

_____ (p.x)   *Help* Others and Give Back

_____ (p.114) Be more *Hopeful and Optimistic*
        (p.116) How To: Nurture an Optimistic Outlook
        (p.117) Use Benefit Finding
        (p.119) Use Benefit Remembering
        (p.119) Use Downward Comparisons

_____ (p.120) Undertake a *Meaning-Making Mission*

_____ (p.173) Use *Meditation* (Self-compassion and Loving Kindness)

_____ (p.135) Create a Resilient *Mindset*

_____ (p.153) Take a *News Holiday*

_____ (p.152) Improve *People-Picking Skills*

_____ (p.132) Reduce *Perfectionism*

_____ (p.52) Identify *Personal Problems*
(p.52) How To: Be a Good Social Problem-Solver

_____ (p.64) Use *Pets*

_____ (p.149) How To: Begin to *Plan* Your Next Steps

_____ (p.68) Increase *Positive Emotions*
(p.68) Create a "Bucket List": Schedule Fun Activities
(p.66) How To: Increase Positive Emotions

_____ (p.73) Use *Positive Humor*

_____ (p.105) How To: Steps to Becoming More *Psychologically Flexible*: Adapt and Overcome

_____ (p.55) *Read Helpful Books*: Access Role Models

_____ (p.43) *Reconnect* with social supports

_____ (p.76) How To: *Regulate Negative Emotions* and Use Opposite Actions
(p.111) How to Look at Things Differently

_____ (p.43) Stay connected and *Reintegrate*

_____ (p.54) Improve *Relationship Skills*
(p.54) How To: Nurture My Relationship with My Partner or Spouse

_____ (p.90) *Relax* and stay calm under pressure
(p.93) How To: Do Mindfulness
(p.94) How To: Use Tactical Breathing

_____ (p.41) *Renegotiate Roles* and Responsibilities

_____ (p.62) Use healing *Rituals*

_____ (p.131) Avoid *Ruminating and Brooding*

_____ (p.145) Use daily *Safe Routines*

_____ (p.148) Bolster *Self-Confidence*

_____ (p.100) Change my *Self-Talk*

_____ (p.83) *Share my story*

_____ (p.30) *Sleep Better*
>   (p.30) How To: Improve Sleep Behavior
>   (p.33) How To: Deal with nightmares

_____ (p.8) Assess my *Strengths* (Post Traumatic Growth)

_____ (p.102) Become *"Stress Hardy"*

_____ (p.101) How To: *Talk Back* to My Brain Differently

_____ (p.131) Avoid *Thinking Traps*
>   (p.132) Can You Identify the Following 'Thinking Traps' in Your
>   Self-Talk
>   (p.133) How Perfectionistic Are You?

_____ (p.71) Develop a *True Grit* attitude

_____ (p.177) Identify *Values* and *Strengths* (H-SLIDER)

_____ (p.156) Access *Websites* and *Community Resources*

_____ (p.85) Use *"Writing Cure"* and *Journaling*
>   (p.87) How To: Journal and Engage in Guided Reconsideration

References

Adler, A.M., Bliese, P.D. & Castro, C.A. (Eds.). (2011). *Deployment psychology*. Washington, DC: American Psychological Association.

Ainspan, N.D. & Penk, W.E. (Eds.). (2008). *Returning wars' wounded, injured and ill: A reference handbook*. Westport, CT: Greenwood Publishing Group.

Alvord, M.K., Zucker, B. & Grados, J.J. (2011). *Resilience builder program for children and adolescents*. Champaign, IL: Research Press.

Antony, M.M. & Swinson, R.P. (1998). *When perfectionism isn't good enough: Strategies for coping with perfectionism*. Oakland, CA: New Harbinger Publications.

Armstrong, K., Best, S. & Domenici, P. (2006*). Courage after fire: coping strategies for troops returning from Iraq and Afghanistan and their families*. Berkeley, CA: Ulysses Press.

Bearak, B. (2012, February 15). The living nightmare: Quanitta Underwood: A contender for olympic gold and a survivor. Retrieved from *http://www.nytimes.com/2012/02/12/ sports/quanitta-underwood-a-contender-for-olympic-gold-and-a-survivor.html?pagewanted=all*

Bonnano, G.A. (2004). Loss, trauma, and human resilience: have we underestimated the human capacity to thrive after extremely aversive events. *American Psychologist, 59.* 20-28.

Borysenko, J. (2009*). It's not the end of the world: Developing resilience in times of change*. Carlsbad, CA: Hay House.

Briere, J. and Scott, C. (2006). *Principles of trauma therapy: A guide to symptoms, evaluation and treatment*. Thousand Oaks, CA: Sage Publications.

Brom, D., Pat-Horencyzk, R. & Ford, J.D. (Eds.). (2009). *Treating traumatized children: Risk, resilience and recovery*. New York: Routledge.

Brooks, R. and Goldstein, S. (2003). *The power of resilience: Achieving balance, confidence, and personal strength in your life*. New York: McGraw-Hill.

Buergenthal, T. (2009). *A lucky child: A memoir of surviving Auschwitz as a young boy*. New York: Little Brown & Co.

Calhoun, L.G. & Tedeschi, R.G. (Eds.). (2006). *Handbook of posttraumatic growth: Research and practice*. Mahwah, NJ: Lawrence Erlbaum.

Duckworth, A. L., Petersen, L., Matthews, M.D., & Kelly, D.R. (2007) Grit: Perserverence and passion for long-term goals. *Journal of Personality and Social Psychology*, 82, 1087-1101.

Dweck, C. (2012). *Mindset: How you can fulfill your potential*. London: Constable & Robinson Limited.

Ehlers, A. & Clark, D.M. (2000). A cognitive model of posttraumatic stress disorder. *Behavior Research and Therapy*, 38. 319-345.

Enright, R.D. (2001). *Forgiveness is choice: A step-by-step process for resolving anger and restoring hope*. Washington, DC: American Psychological Association.

Etter, D.A. Ch (LTC). (Fall 2007). A chaplain's reflections on combat experience offers insights into returning veterans' needs. *Resource Links*, 6 (1), 5-6.

Flannery, R.B. (1992). *Posttraumatic stress disorder: The victim's guide to healing and recovery*. New York: Crossroad Press.

Frankl, V.E. (1985). *Man's search for meaning*. New York: Washington Square Press.

Fredrickson, B. L., Tugade, M.M. (2001). Positive emotions and emotional intelligence. In Feldman B.L. & Salovey, P. (2001). *The wisdom of feelings: processes underlying emotional intelligence*. (pp. 321). New York: Guilford.

Freeman, S., Moore, B. & Freeman, A. (2009). *Living and surviving in harm's way: A psychological treatment handbook for pre and post deployment of military personnel*. New York: Routledge.

Harvey, M.R. & Tummala-Narra, P. (Eds.). (2007). *Sources and expressions of resilience in trauma survivors*. Binghamton, NY: Haworth Press.

Hall, L.K. (2008). *Counseling military families: What mental health professionals need to know*. New York: Routledge.

Joseph, S. (2011). *What doesn't kill us: The new psychology of posttraumatic growth*. New York: Basic Books.

Joseph, S., Linky, P.A. (Eds.). (2008). *Trauma, recovery and growth: Positive psychological perspectives on posttraumatic stress*. Hoboken, NJ: Wiley.

Kabat-Zinn, J. (1990). *Full catastrophic living. Using the wisdom of your body and mind to face stress, pain and illness*. New York: Dell.

Kabat-Zinn, J. (1994). *Wherever you go, there you are: Mindfulness meditation in everyday life*. New York: Hyperion.

Koerner, R. & Linehan, M.M. (2011). *Doing dialectical behavior therapy: A practical guide*. New York: Guilford Press.

Kubany, E.S. (1994). A cognitive model of guilt typology in combat-related PTSD. *Journal of Traumatic Stress*, 7. 3-19.

Kubany, E.S., Ralston, T.C. (2008). *Treating PTSD in battered women: A step-by-step manual for therapists and counselors*. Oakland, CA: New Harbinger Publications.

Kushner, H.S. (1981). *When bad things happen to good people*. New York: Schocken Books.

Lord, W. 1993. *Incredible victory: The battle of midway*. New York: HarperCollins.

Love, P & Shulkin, S. (2003). *How to ruin a perfectly good relationship*. Phoenix: Zeig, Tucker & Theisen.

Lyubomirsky, S. (2008). *The how of happiness: A scientific approach to getting the life you want*. New York: Pergamon Press.

Maddi, S. & Kobasa, S. (1984). *The hardy executive: Health under stress* (2nd ed.). Columbus, OH. McGraw-Hill.

Masten, A. (2001). Ordinary magic: Resilience process in development. *American Psychologist, 56*. 227-238.

Meichenbaum, D. (2009). Bolstering resilience: Benefiting from lessons learned. In D. Brom, R. Pat-Horencyzk and J.D. Ford. (2009). *Treating traumatized children: Risk, resilience and recovery*. (pp. 183-192). New York: Routledge.

Meichenbaum, D. (2006). Resilience and posttraumatic growth: A constructive narrative perspective. In L.G. Calhoun & R.G. Tedeshi (Eds.). (2006). *Handbook of posttraumatic growth: Research and practice* (pp. 355-368). New York: Taylor & Francis, Inc.

Meichenbaum, D. (2011). Resiliency building as a means to prevent PTSD and related adjustment problems in military personnel. In B.A. Moore & W.E. Penk (Eds.). (2011) *Treating PTSD in military personnel: A clinical handbook* (pp. 325-344). New York: Guilford Press.

Meredith, L.S., Sherbourne, C.D., Gaillot, S., Hansell, L., Richard, H.V., Parker, A.M. & Wrenn, G. (2011). *Promoting psychological resilience in the U.S. Military*. Santa Monica: Rand Corporation.

Metcalf, L. (2004). *The miracle question: Answer it and change your life*. Bancyfelin, Wales: Crown House Publishing.

Moore, B.A. & Kennedy, C.H. (2011). *Wheels down: Adjusting to life after deployment*. Washington, DC: American Psychological Association.

Morgillo-Freeman, S., Moore, B.A. & Freeman, A. (Eds.). (2009). *Living and surviving in harm's way*. New York: Routledge.

Murphy, R.T. (2008). Enhancing combat veterans' motivation to change Posttraumatic Stress Disorder symptoms and other problem behaviors. In H. Arkowitz, H.A. Westra, W.R. Miller & S. Rollnick (Eds.). *Motivational Interviewing in the treatment of psychological problems* (pp. 57-84). New York: Guilford Press.

Nay, R. (2003). *Taking charge of anger: how to resolve conflict, sustain relationships, and express yourself without losing control*. New York: Guilford Press.

Pargament, K.I. (2007). *Spiritually-integrated psychotherapy: Understanding and addressing the sacred.* New York: Guilford Press.

Penk, W., Little D., and Ainspan, N. (2011). Psychosocial rehabilitation. In B. Moore, W. Penk and M. Friedman (Eds.). (2011). *Treating PTSD in military personnel: A clinical handbook.* (pp. 173-194). New York: Guilford Press.

Pennebaker, J.W. (1997). *Opening up: The healing power of expressing emotions.* New York: Academic Press.

Post, S., Neimark, J. & Moss O. (2007). *Why good things happen to good people: How to live a longer, healthier, happier life by the simple act of giving*: New York: Random House.

Reich, J.W., Zautra, A.J. & Hall, J.S. (Eds.). (2011). *Handbook of adult resilience.* New York: Guilford Press.

Reivich, K. & Shatte, A. (2002). *The resilience factor*. New York: Broadway Books.

Ruzek, J.I., Schnurr, P.P., Vasterling, J.J. & Friedman, M.J. (Eds.) (2011). *Caring for veterans with deployment-related stress disorder.* Washington, DC: American Psychological Association.

Selby, E. A., Anestis, M.D. & Bender, T.W. (2010). Overcoming the fear of lethal injury: Evaluating suicidal behavior in the military through the lens of the Interpersonal–Psychological Theory of Suicide. *Clinical Psychology Review*, 30 (3) 298-307.

Seligman, M.E.P. (2006). *Learned optimism: How to change your mind and your life.* London: Random House.

Sheehy, G. (2003), *Middletown, America: One town's passage from trauma to hope.* New York: Random House.

Sherman, N. (2010), *The untold war: Inside the hearts, minds, and souls of our soldiers.* New York: W.W. Norton.

Slone, L.B. & Friedman, M.J. (2008). *After war zone: A practical guide for returning troops and their families.* Philadelphia, PA: Da Capo Press.

Snyder, C.R. (Ed.). (2002). *Handbook of hope: Theory, measures and applications.* San Diego: Academic Press.

Southwick, S. and Charney, D. S. (2012). *Resilience: The science of mastering life's greatest challenges.* West Nyack, NY: Cambridge University Press.

Waite, T. (1995). *Taken on trust: An autobiography.* New York: William Morrow.

Walsh, F. (2011). *Strengthening family resilience.* New York: Guilford Press.

Wegner, D. (1994). *White bears and other unwanted thoughts: Suppression, obsession and the psychology of mental control.* New York: Guilford Publications

Weiss, T. & Berger, R. (2010). *Posttraumatic growth and culturally competent practice.* New York: John Wiley.

Zayfert, C. & DeViva, J.C. (2011). *When someone you love suffers from posttraumatic stress: What to expect and what you can do.* New York: Guilford Press.

Order Form

ROADMAP TO RESILIENCE:
A GUIDE FOR MILITARY, TRAUMA VICTIMS AND THEIR FAMILIES
Donald Meichenbaum, Ph.D.
224 Pages—Softcover

To order additional copies of this book, you can visit our website, *www.roadmaptoresilience.org*, or send payment by check or money order:

ORDER BY MAIL

Send payment by check or money order to:

Don Meichenbaum
215 Sand Key Estates Drive
Clearwater, Florida 33767

Please make check and money order payable to *Don Meichenbaum* (payable in USD or CAD funds).

ORDER BY CREDIT CARD: (in the US, Canada and Mexico only)

Order online at *www.crownhousepublishing.com* and enter "Roadmap to Resilience" in the search box.

PRICING INFORMATION

In the U.S.: **$41.00 USD** ($35.00 FOR BOOK + $6 shipping and handling.

In Canada: **$50.00 CAD** ($35.00 FOR BOOK + $15.00 AIRMAIL shipping and handling)

In Mexico: **$50.00 USD** ($35.00 FOR BOOK + $15.00 AIRMAIL shipping and handling)

For rest of world: **$55.00 USD** ($35.00 FOR BOOK + $20.00 AIRMAIL shipping and handling)

For inquiries on bulk orders, please contact Don Meichenbaum by email at *dhmeich@aol.com*.

About the Author

Donald Meichenbaum. Ph.D. is a clinical psychologist who has worked for 40 years with traumatized individuals, and most recently with returning service members and their families. He has consulted in a variety of psychiatric facilities and Veteran Administration hospitals creating treatment programs that are designed to help clients with Post Traumatic Stress Disorders, Traumatic Brain Injuries, Substance Abuse, Depression, Suicidality, and other adjustment difficulties.

He has worked with individuals and trained mental health workers in the aftermath of a number of traumatic victimizing experiences including the 9/11 terrorist attack in New York City, school shootings in Columbine, Hurricane Katrina in New Orleans and other such incidents.

He is Distinguished Professor Emeritus, from the University of Waterloo, in Ontario Canada, from which he took early retirement 15 years ago. He then became Research Director of the Melissa Institute for Violence Prevention, in Miami, Florida (see *www.melissainstitute.org)*.

He is one of the founders of cognitive behavior therapy and in a survey of clinicians he was voted "one of the 10 most influential psychotherapists of the twentieth century." He has published extensively and has presented in all of the 50 United States and internationally. He has received a Lifetime Achievement Award from the Clinical Division of the American Psychological Association. He has been Distinguished Visiting Professor at the University of Miami, School of Education.

He has brought all of this experience together in creating *Roadmap to Resilience.* For additional papers visit *www.melissainstitute.org* Website and click on Author Index on the Homepage and scroll to Meichenbaum. Click on papers of interest.

211